GOD AND EVOLUTION

GOD AND EVOLUTION

R. J. BERRY, D.Sc., F.R.S.E.

Professor of Genetics at
University College London

Hodder & Stoughton
LONDON SYDNEY AUCKLAND TORONTO

Scripture quotations in this publication are from the Holy Bible, New International Version. Copyright © 1973, 1978, 1984 International Bible Society. Published by Hodder & Stoughton.

British Library Cataloguing in Publication Data
Berry, R. J.
    God and evolution.
    1. Human evolution—Religious aspects
    I. Title
    213   GN281.4

ISBN 0 340 34249 8

Contents

In the beginning

Consider what God has done:
Who can straighten what he has made crooked?
When times are good, be happy; but when times are bad,
consider: God has made the one as well as the other.
                                            Ecclesiastes 7:13,14

Every Christian has to decide at some time how to resolve the apparent conflict between the scientific and scriptural accounts of the origin of the world and its inhabitants. Some believe that the Genesis stories of creation are not to be taken seriously, while others argue that current scientific interpretations must err if they do not agree with biblical revelation. Both approaches produce problems, perhaps most acutely in teenagers or students brought up to accept the Bible as authoritative, but given a coherent account of geological and biological evolution at school or college.

This book is about the arguments over creation and evolution. It is a re-written version of a book I produced thirteen years ago (*Adam and the Ape*. Falcon, 1975). My aim then was simply apologetic: to help Christians understand the truths behind the evolution debate. However the last decade has seen an aggressive propagation of "creationist"[1] ideas, and a denigration of so-called theistic evolution

---

[1] Throughout the book I have put "creationist" and "creationism" in inverted commas to emphasise that the words are now being used in a very restricted sense. All Christians who profess "I believe in God . . . maker of heaven and earth" are properly called creationists in the full sense of the word.

(which is based on the scripturally-derived belief that God normally acts in and through scientifically studiable processes which can be studied scientifically), and the time has come for a fuller treatment.

The traditional understanding of the Bible was that God made the world and all that is in it during a six day period a few thousand years ago. Indeed, many Bibles head the marginal notes of the first chapter of Genesis with the date 4004 BC. This timing was calculated by Archbishop Ussher of Armagh (who rather appropriately was also Professor of Theological Controversies at Trinity College Dublin) in a book (*Annals of the Ancient and New Testaments*) published in 1650, by the simple method of adding up the ages of all the people in the biblical genealogies from Adam to Christ. John Lightfoot, Vice-Chancellor of Cambridge University and a contemporary of Ussher's, went further, and deduced that creation was completed at 9.00 a.m. on Sunday, 23rd October.

Ussher's arithmetic is perfectly sound. (Add up the ages of the patriarchs given in Genesis, chapters 5, 11 and 19, and you get a figure of 2,046 years from the creation of Adam to the age of Abraham at the time of the birth of Isaac. The time of Abraham can be dated from several independent archaeological sources: according to the *New Bible Dictionary* it was around 2000 to 1850 BC.) The difficulty is that it places Adam as living at a time when there was already considerable urban civilisation in the Middle East, thus lessening his claim to be the founder of the whole human race.

Most people nowadays do not accept Ussher's interpretation, and reject the whole literalist interpretation of the Bible from which it sprang. The unfortunate thing – and this is the reason why the question is important – is that in disbelieving one way of looking at one part of creation, such people tend also to throw away the Creator who is revealed in the early chapters of the Bible and make the man created in His image no different from any other animal. Since these chapters deal in a particularly explicit way with the work of God in His world, the result is an understanding of a god so far removed from everyday living that he is hardly worth believing in.

This confusion about God and His work is really the subject of this book. My theme is that the whole creation debate is worthwhile if it leads us to a more reverent and scriptural idea of God than that of a cosmic mechanic or a blind watchmaker (p. 42). Such a god is far too small!

God and Evolution is a lot more forthright about "creationism" than was *Adam and the Ape*. Repeatedly over the past few years I have counselled people perplexed because of the dogmatism of "creationists" over particular *interpretations* of scripture, and who have begun to doubt the connection of God the Creator with God the Redeemer and Sustainer; time after time I have had to help Christians so confused about the relationship of Creator and creation that they have virtually got to the point of renouncing their Christian faith as irrelevant and irrational. I argue in chapter 7, that the compulsion to "creationism" does not stem primarily from either accurate exegesis or faulty science, but from a simple fear of change; the conflict is thus resolvable by moral challenge, not by objective analysis. This diagnosis could be wrong, but it seems to be the only explanation which fits all the facts (including Bible truth).

It follows that I am highly critical about many of the claims of "creationists". It is both uncomfortable and pastorally hazardous to criticise those who love the Lord and His Word, but it is right to do so if such people hinder the young or pervert the truth. I hope I have given enough information about evolution and creation for those with open minds to make their own decisions on the topics dealt with in this book. I have sought to deal with all the key issues, based on my reading of both evolutionary and religious writings, but almost inevitably there will be questions unanswered that some will regard as critical.

Some things that I have written in this book will offend. I am sorry, but unrepentant. Primarily I am concerned with truth, both scientific and scriptural; truth which is not academic and sterile, but which affects our relation to and reliance on God. This is a pastoral book, not a work of scholarship. Notwithstanding, *God and Evolution* has to justify its arguments, and I have had to dig more deeply into some issues than I did in *Adam and the Ape*, in which my aim was essentially didactic. This means that I shall irritate some who will feel that I have included too much science or history or sociology. To all these, my response is that I have tried to suggest enough references to fill out topics which I may have under-emphasised; and anyone can skip sections which they feel to be irrelevant. I summarise the main points of the book on p. 163; that should be clear to all.

What about my own qualifications for writing? As a research scientist I am professionally concerned about the mechanisms affecting variation in animal populations, and which thus form a major part of evolutionary studies; as Professor of Genetics in the University of London I am charged with teaching about genetical and evolutionary problems; from 1982–5 I was President of the Linnean Society of London, the oldest biological society in the world, at which Charles Darwin's and Alfred Russel Wallace's papers on evolution by natural selection were read in 1858; I am currently President of the British Ecological Society. It is more difficult to proclaim one's Christian orthodoxy. I am a licensed Reader in the Church of England and Chairman of the Research Scientists' Christian Fellowship, a section of the University and Colleges Christian Fellowship Associates. More relevantly I am a Christian acknowledging Jesus Christ as Lord and Liberator, and the Holy Scriptures as the supreme authority in all matters of faith and conduct.

Charles Darwin was the founder of evolutionary theory as we know it today. In the last paragraph of the *Origin of Species* (1859), the book which first described his evolutionary ideas, Darwin wrote: "It is interesting to contemplate an entangled bank, clothed with many plants of many kinds, with birds singing on the bushes with various insects flitting about, and with worms crawling through the damp earth, and to reflect that these elaborately constructed forms, so different from each other, in so complex a

manner, have all been produced by laws acting around us."
Not so very different from the awe of David in Psalm 19; it
is as good an introduction as any to *God and Evolution*,
which is about Creation *and* Evolution, not Creation *or*
Evolution.

1

Does evolution matter?

One can be a Christian and an evolutionist, just as one can be a Christian thief, or a Christian adulterer, or a Christian liar. It is absolutely impossible for those who profess to believe the Bible and to follow Christ to embrace evolutionism.
　　　　　Henry Morris in *King of Creation* (1980)
I see no good reason why the views given in this volume should shock the religious feelings of anyone.
　　　　　Charles Darwin in *The Origin of Species* (1859)
There is a proper time and procedure for every matter.
　　　　　Ecclesiastes 8:6

Why is evolution such a red rag to many Christians? Is it impossible for an orthodox, Bible-believing Christian to be an evolutionist? What is all the fuss about?

The answers to these questions will take the rest of this book to answer, but we can begin very simply by stating that the argument is not so much about the scientific theory of evolution (although many people are confused about this, and biological evolution is mixed up with "evolutionism" and a gaggle of other "isms" – racialism, capitalism, socialism, sexism, and others), as about the proper *understanding* of the Bible, particularly the creation stories in the first two chapters of Genesis. It is also worth saying that the apparent lack of books by evolutionist Christians is not because such Christians do not exist but because those who are informed about the issues tend not to be skilled in debating problems which they regard as long settled, and therefore a waste of time in reopening. After all, did not Paul warn Timothy to avoid endless genealogies? "These promote controversies rather than God's work – which is by faith" [1 Timothy 1:4]; and evolution as debated by Christians tends to be about descent and relationships, in other words about genealogies. Although we are sometimes told that a large and increasing number of scientists are questioning the truth of evolution, most of the vocal anti-evolutionary scientists are engineers, physicists or chemists; there are almost no professional biologists (i.e. those who are concerned with the study of evolution and its problems) among them. (Dorothy Nelkin [1982: 84–90] lists the prominent "creationist" activists and their qualifications; according to Bridgstock [1986a:14] the Creation Science Foundation of Australia had seven members in 1984 – two missionaries, one teacher, one solicitor, two medical practitioners, and one accountant.) This is not to deny that there is an entirely proper debate about the mechanism(s) of evolution going on among biologists; we shall discuss this in chapter 5. But it is important to emphasise that those who debate the origins of life (p. 98) like Chandra Wickramasinghe and Fred Hoyle, or cladism (p. 100) like Gareth Nelson and Colin Patterson, or punctuated equilibria (p. 97) like Niles Eldredge and Stephen Gould, are concerned about particular parts of evolutionary theory, not about the fact that evolution occurred.

Notwithstanding, there are many Christians who cannot see how the loving God of the Bible can also be the controller of a creation characterised by chance and conflict, or accept that the man created in God's image is related to the apes; and there are non-Christians who find faith in a God who somehow brought into being the whole universe as we know it a mere 6,000 years ago to be wholly incredible. For both these groups it is right to enquire what scientists actually know about evolution, and what is guess-work; what the Bible actually tells us about creation; and how much we unjustifiably assume because we have never thought about other possible interpretations.

The Bible and science

It is as well to get certain misunderstandings out of the way as soon as possible. On the door of the old Cavendish Laboratory in Cambridge where many facts about the fundamental nature of matter were discovered, is the research scientists' text: "Great are the works of the Lord; they are pondered by all who delight in them" [Psalm 111:2]. This will appear odd to these who think of scientists in almost the same breath as anti-Christ, and believe that science claims to have disproved the Bible.

There are two answers to this. The first is that scientists are no less likely to be Christians than are farmers, hairdressers or policemen, and indeed scientists are in some ways more likely to accept Christian truth because their whole training is concerned with evaluating facts and making decisions about their implications. There are many scientists who see their work as in a very real sense "studying the works of the Lord".

More important however is the need to recognise that there are only three points where scientific knowledge and method contact the contents of the Bible. These are:

1. Miracles
2. Origins
3. Man

Evolution is involved in all these contact points. We shall have to enquire if evolution is likely to have happened, and if so, whether it is merely a blind, mechanistic process or whether God operated in and through the process; what conflicts there are between the biological and scriptural accounts of the origin of matter, life and man; and if man is nothing more than a naked ape, or whether we are in any real sense made "in God's image".

There are, of course, other contact points between the

Bible and secular knowledge. Most of them concern the historical truth of Bible statements. More and more, archaeological and historical research is confirming the Bible record. This is a fascinating story in itself, but not what this book is about. What we shall be doing (especially in chapter 3) is to summarise what science can tell us about scientific and Bible accounts of the same process.

However, before we launch into a detailed discussion of the relationship between science and the Bible, we must clear away a very common misapprehension about the nature of science and its influence on Bible truth; we must dispose of the fallacy of "nothing buttery".

Scientists study *how* things work: what causes plants to grow, animals to mate, minerals to form, and so on. They do this by testing an idea (or *hypothesis*) by means of experiments or other information (from history, other tested hypotheses, etc.). The more tests a hypothesis survives without being disproved, the more likely it is to be right. The historians' date for the beginning of modern science is 1543, because two books were published in that year which marked the end of the mediaeval tradition of uncritically accepting tradition and the start of rigorous examination of ideas by experiment, which is the basis of true science. (The two books were Copernicus' *Revolution of the Heavenly Bodies* and Vesalius' *Anatomy of the Human Body*.) Ever since 1543, our knowledge of the natural world has grown at an ever-increasing rate; although there is still much that we do not know, it is true to claim that we have a fairly clear understanding of the way that the world works.

As scientific knowledge has advanced it has brought with it a wholly false assumption: that if we know *one* cause of an event we know everything about that event. This assumption is not true. A simple analogy may help: we can describe a painting entirely in terms of the distribution of chemical molecules in two dimensional space. If we knew enough about pigment chemistry, we could give a complete description of that picture in chemical terms. But we can also give a complete description of the same picture in terms of its design and composition, telling why the artist created it as he did. Both our two descriptions refer to the same physical object; both are complete in themselves, yet they do not overlap at all. It is obviously inadequate to describe the picture as *nothing but* a collection of spatially ordered chemicals; it is equally untrue to assert that it is *nothing but* an artistic design. Obviously our picture has more than one "cause".

The idea that an event has more than one cause is at least as old as Aristotle, who distinguished material and efficient causes (which answer the question "how?") from formal and final causes (which answer the question "why?"). The fallacy of "nothing buttery" is to believe that we know everything about an event when we can answer the question "how".

The tragedy is that we assume that scientists have excluded God from the world if we can answer "how" questions without referring to Him; we assume that there is less and less room for God in our world as we know more and more about how it works. God is squeezed into the ever-decreasing gaps in our knowledge. Put another way, since 1543 God has been progressively confined to events we cannot yet explain. The only way to keep such a God in the universe is to make Him ever smaller. A few years ago it was fashionable to say that God controlled the position of electrons, which theory ("Heisenberg's uncertainty principle") states it is impossible to predict, but this approach is not very convincing: either He is Lord of all, or He is not Lord at all.

The truth is that science is only concerned with "how" questions; although it is possible to ask some "why" questions (for example, why insect-pollinated flowers are brightly coloured, or why herring gulls have red spots on their beak), in general there are many questions which it is meaningless for a scientist to ask. Sir Peter Medawar, a Nobel laureate for his work in immunology, has stated the situation clearly:

That there is indeed a limit upon science is made very likely by the existence of questions that science cannot answer and that no conceivable advances of science would empower it to answer. These are the questions children ask – the ultimate questions of Karl Popper. I have in mind such questions as:

How did everything begin?
What are we all here for?
What is the point of living?

Doctrinaire positivism – now something of a period piece – dismissed all such questions as nonquestions or pseudoquestions such as only simpletons ask and only charlatans of one kind or another profess to be able to answer. This peremptory dismissal leaves one empty and dissatisfied because the questions make sense to those who ask them, and the answers to those who give them; but whatever else may be in dispute, it would be universally agreed that it is not to science that we should look for answers. There is then a prima-facie case for the existence of a limit to scientific understanding. [Medawar, 1984: 66]

This can be illustrated by miracles: a scientist cannot prove that miracles do not happen, because by definition a miracle is not a predicted response to a particular set of conditions. Conversely, he can never prove that miracles *do* occur. He may record events for which he has no explanation, but he is unable to state whether he is ignorant or whether a miracle has occurred. Science can say very little about miracles [Berry, 1986b: see Appendix, p. 165].

Similarly, science can never prove or disprove the existence of God, unless one property of matter or some behaviour was shown to be completely impossible if God did not exist. The Book of Hebrews is explicit that "By faith we understand that the universe was formed at God's command, so that what is seen was not made out of what was visible" [Hebrews 11:3]. God is apprehended through faith, not rational understanding.

Science can tell us very little about God. It is certainly untrue that scientists have "disproved God" or anything like it. There is no way that they could do that. And we shall see when we examine the question of evolution that it has very little to do with God or anti-God, although the implications and assumptions of the theory can be very relevant to faith and behaviour.

Apes and Genesis

The one bit of Darwinian history that almost everyone knows is the confrontation between Bishop Samuel Wilberforce and Thomas Henry Huxley at the 1860 British Association meeting in Oxford. It is unfortunate that Wilberforce was a Christian and Huxley was not, because the evolution debate became a religion *versus* science argument from that moment on, whereas the British Association meeting really showed the death-throes of an outmoded understanding of the world, rather incidentally supported by some bad theology.

We shall come back later to both the scientific and theological questions. For the moment, let us recall the climax of Wilberforce's lecture, when he allegedly turned to Huxley and asked "whether it was through his grandfather or his grandmother that he claimed descent from a monkey", to which Huxley is said to have replied (no full record exists of the occasion) that "if I had to choose between a poor ape for an ancestor and a man highly endowed by nature and of great influence, who used those gifts to introduce ridicule into scientific discussion and to discredit humble seekers after truth, I would affirm my preference for an ape". Benjamin Disraeli expressed the extremes in this exchange when he wrote in 1860 "Is man an ape or an angel? I am on the side of the angels."

For those who have followed the previous section on the relation between religious and scientific truth, it should be clear that both Wilberforce and Disraeli were falling into the fallacy of "nothing buttery". As any biologist or doctor can testify, we are anatomically, physiologically and genetically very like the surviving apes (chimpanzees, orang utans, etc.). This does not mean that we are therefore *nothing but* an ape. The Genesis 1 account of creation describes a progress from chaos through an increasing biological complexity to man who is said to have been created along with "cattle and creeping things and beasts of the earth" on the sixth day of creation. But man was distinguished from the other animals by being made "in God's image". This is even more explicit in the Genesis 2 account, where man is a two-stage creation: God took material which He had previously made and "breathed into his nostrils the breath of life: and man became a living being". In other words we have both continuity with and distinctness from other animals.

There is nothing new or radical in claiming that we are *both* animals *and* spiritual beings. Calvin recognised this explicitly: "Man is linked with the natural creation by his body being made of the same substance as the rest of creation." Yet he is distinct from it, because God endues this substance "with a soul, whence it received vital motion; and on this soul engraved his own image, to which immortality is annexed".

If we follow Disraeli and argue that man is *either* an ape whose origins and nature can be studied by science *or* an angel specially created by God, we are going to have problems. My argument is that philosophy, biology and Scripture all testify to the possibility that we can regard humankind as genetically related to other animals, most closely to the apes; but that we also recognise *by faith* the work of God in making us "in His image".

The origin of man (and woman) is something on which scientists have spoken with some dogmatism because there are fossils which to some extent link apes and man (*Dryopithecus, Ramapithecus, Australopithecus, Homo habilis, H. erectus*, etc). "Creationists" have objected that this fossil succession is characterised more by gaps and guesses than anything else [see Bowden, M., 1977]. I discuss the origin of man in chapter 4, and argue there that God in some sense "took over" a pre-man at a particular time in history, and that man became Adam. But, and this is important, when we are faced with scientific accounts of the evolution of man, there is no reason at all to assume that the change from pre-man to Adam would have any anatomical consequences at all. We can study human origins as an anthropological or as a theological question. For a full understanding of ourselves we must regard the answers we obtain as complementary; there is no need whatsoever to assume that the answers to anthropological questions will contradict the answers to theological ones, or that theologians will necessarily be at odds with anthropologists [Berry, 1987].

In principle we might expect to be able to learn from science more about the origin of man than about the earlier origins of life or matter. Notwithstanding, the same principles apply and if, for example, someone managed to "make life" in the laboratory, this would not in any way reduce the significance of the original creation of life, nor affect by one iota the likelihood of God's involvement.

The unimportance of evolution for Christians

Salvation does not depend upon assent to or dissent from any claim of science. Nor does it depend on belief in the truth or inspiration of the Bible. Salvation is through faith in Christ alone; it is shown by the works of the Spirit in our life.

Once we have become Christians, we are committed to a God who reveals Himself to men, and as Christ Himself confirmed, one of the most important ways He does this is in the Bible (Luke 18:31; John 5:39; etc). Our acceptance of Christ as Saviour leads us to acknowledge the authority of Scripture – including the creation narratives of Genesis. But this is a consequence of salvation, not a condition of it.

In a similar way, when we work out the meaning of our Christian faith, we soon come to recognise the sovereignty of God over all of life, and our own weakness and incapacity when we see ourselves alongside Him. It is both impertinent and implausible to think of ourselves as achieving goodness without Him. Indeed, if this was possible, there would have been no need for Christ to die for us. This means that the idea of an evolutionary humanism with man continually improving morally is inconsistent with biblical Christianity. But evolutionary humanism is not the same thing as biological evolution; it is a philosophical interpretation of it.

In just the same way, it is up to Christians to interpret biological evolution in the light of Scripture. There is no biological reason why God should not have intervened in history to make man in His own image, nor why that man should not have rebelled, and stand in need of redemption. In other words, biological evolution itself is of no importance to Christians; it is how we interpret it. That is what this book is about.

2

The idea of evolution

I turned my mind to understand, to investigate and to search out . . . the scheme of things.

Ecclesiastes 7:25

From Plato to the nineteenth century

Darwin did not invent evolution. And it was not Darwin's ideas that suddenly made evolution plausible in the mid-nineteenth century. Historians have claimed to find evolutionary ideas expressed by many different scholars, from at least the time of Aristotle on. However, it was only in the eighteenth century that naturalists really began to grapple with the possibility of biological change and men like Buffon and Lamarck are probably best regarded as the earliest evolutionists in the modern sense.

Plato (c. 427–347 BC)

The greatest influence on evolutionary thought from classical (i.e. Roman-Greek) times onwards until the nineteenth century was the philosopher Plato, c. 427–347 BC, and his influence was entirely negative. The [OED] dictionary definition of evolution includes "the process of unrolling or opening out; developing from a rudimentary to a complete state". In other words, evolution involves change; Plato rooted himself in a mathematically derived obsession for an unchanging universal reality. Four of his ideas, based in theoretical metaphysics rather than observational science, have had a particularly deleterious effect on biology:

1. A belief that the world we live in was nothing but an expression of a limited number of fixed and unchanging forms. Plato called them *essences*. Variation was regarded as the result of imperfect manifestation of the essences.
2. A concept that the whole cosmos was a living harmonious whole, like an individual animal. Any change would disturb the harmony.
3. The idea of a creative power, called a demiurge. Plato was a polytheist and pagan, but Christianity took over Plato's demiurge as its creator God. This interpretation controlled the later Christian tradition of natural theology, and the assumption that a prime task of philosophers was to reveal "the blueprint of the creator".
4. A stress on "soul" as a non-material entity. When this was merged with Bible teaching, Christian belief made it extremely difficult to accept that humans and their soul had a place in an evolutionary scheme.

Philosophers and theologians delight in arguing about the importance of people like Plato for later thought. These discussions are not relevant here. The point worth making is that however much subsequent scholars have adopted or dissociated themselves from Plato's ideas, there can be no dispute that they fitted beautifully into a Christian scheme, based upon an unchanging God who created a world which was "very good" (in the words of Genesis), but which has been disrupted by human sinfulness. Equally, there is no doubt that Plato's assertion of an unchanging, underlying reality meant that evolution was impossible to fit into the accepted understanding of the world. The world-picture developed by the early and mediaeval Church was static and idealised because it incorporated so many ideas from

Greek philosophy, and this was reflected in the interpretation of Scripture.

Aristotle (384–322 BC)

The greatest Greek naturalist was Aristotle (384–322 BC). He was educated by some of the best doctors of his day. Later in life he spent three years on the island of Lesbos, where he evidently devoted much time to marine biology. He was the first to give detailed life histories for a large number of species; he wrote a whole book on reproductive biology and life cycles. He was immensely interested in organic diversity (i.e. the enormous variety of living organisms) and the reasons for it. Although he did not propose a formal classification, he classified animals by specific criteria, and his arrangement of the invertebrates was better than that of Linnaeus, two thousand years later. Far more than his predecessors, he was an observer and experimenter. He stated explicitly that the information one receives from the senses is more important than what reason tells one. In that respect he was a world apart from later so-called Aristotleans, who simply and solely rationalised about all their problems.

Aristotle described a fairly continuous progression in the organisation and complexity of living nature. Indeed, he thought that "nature passes from inanimate objects through plants to animals in an unbroken sequence". Later writers identified this as a *scala naturae* or Great Chain of Being, but Aristotle was not an evolutionist. He saw a steady-state in nature, maintained by a continual progression of birth followed by death. He recognised well-defined and unchanging species. His gradation of living things was a static concept to him, and he explicitly rejected the "evolution" theory of Empedocles (who thought that everything was composed of varying amounts of earth, air, fire, and water).

Early Christianity

Christianity as revealed in the Bible and interpreted by

first Jewish and then Christian scholars, was grafted on to a Greek understanding of the world. The Bible spoke of an almighty creator who had made the world out of nothing in six days, six thousand years ago (based on various Old Testament genealogies). There was apparently no time for change to have taken place; the world as we know it was essentially the same as it had been at the time of its creation. And for the first fifteen centuries of Christianity there was no reason to challenge this interpretation.

The beginning of modern science

Science in the modern sense began in the sixteenth century, stimulated by the sense of personal responsibility towards God and his creation inculcated by the rediscovery of the Bible in the Reformation. The most important early developments were in the physical sciences. The Greek concept of the universe as an organism with a soul was gradually replaced by a machine kept going by a set of laws, like that of gravity. The creator became a designer and originator, rather than overall controller. God was still the first cause for everything that exists, but all natural processes were regulated by "secondary causes" exemplified by scientific (or "natural") laws. The explanation of all natural phenomena by such laws became the goal of science.

This new way of thinking was particularly successful in astronomy. The old universe was of a very limited size. The invention of the telescope put an end to this: the more powerful telescopes became, the further the "heavens" seemed to expand. The idea that the universe could be regarded as almost infinitely large became accepted.

Even more profound changes in interpretation took place in the science we now call geology. In particular, evidence began to accumulate that the surface of the earth had not always been the same. One of the first pointers was the discovery of extinct volcanoes in central France, which led to the recognition that basalt, a widely distributed rock, is nothing but ancient lava. At about the same time, it was realised that many – indeed most – geological strata are sedimentary, deposited from water, and sometimes these deposits may be tens of thousands of feet thick. This was extremely disturbing: it must have taken an immense amount of time for such thick strata to be deposited, so the earth must be much older than previously thought. Even worse was the discovery that neither the volcanic nor the sedimentary rocks had remained unchanged after being laid down. They were subsequently eroded by water cutting valleys through them, and in many cases sedimentary layers were folded and occasionally turned completely over at some time after deposition.

All of this stimulated interest in the age of the earth. Newton – who was a convinced but heterodox Christian – calculated that the earth must have cooled for at least 50,000 years until it was cold enough for life, but he felt that something must be wrong with his sums because this was so much greater than the Church's teaching of 6,000 years since creation.

In *Les Époches de la Nature* [1779], Buffon (Director of the Royal Botanic Garden in Paris 1739–1788) reported on some experiments he had done heating a group of spheres of various sizes, from which he concluded that 74,832 years were required for the cooling of the earth from white heat to its present condition. (He privately estimated that the earth was at least half a million years old, but did not publish this figure, because an earlier book of his had been censored.) In an attempt to harmonise his results with Scripture, Buffon argued that there had been seven epochs of earth history matching the days of creation in Genesis. In other words, he suggested, his interpretation was not all that different from the traditional one, so long as the Genesis days were taken as "epochs" rather than twenty-four hour periods:

1. Formation of the earth and planets.
2. Origination of the great mountain ranges.
3. Water covering all dry land.
4. Beginning of volcanic activity.
5. Elephants and other tropical animals inhabiting the north temperate area familiar to Buffon.

6. Separation of continents (Buffon appreciated the similarity of North American animals to those of Europe and Asia, and reasoned that the two land masses must have been connected with each other at some time in the past).
7. Appearance of man.

Another problem for the eighteenth-century understanding of the Genesis story was the ever-increasing knowledge of fossils. Fossils were, of course, well known, but for a long time they were believed to be nothing more than an accident of nature (*lusus naturae*) rather than the remains of once-living creatures. As time passed, the organic origin of fossils became increasingly accepted. The last capable naturalist to advocate an inorganic origin seems to have been Johann Beringer of the University of Würzburg. Beringer loved to collect and sketch fossils, but was convinced that they were simply curious shapes produced by nature. His *Lithographiae Wirceburgiensis* [1726] contained drawings and descriptions of all manner of objects dug from local quarries including many genuine fossils, but also images of birds sitting on their nests, entirely imaginary animals, and Hebrew letters. Such extremely odd discoveries confirmed Beringer in his belief that fossils were not buried organisms, until one day he discovered a rock with his own likeness and name on it. The perpetrators of the hoax, jealous of Beringer's reputation, had baked and carved fake fossils and planted them in Beringer's favourite collecting spots. Beringer spent the rest of his life attempting to recall all the published copies of his book.

However, the common explanation for fossils was that they represented creatures drowned in Noah's flood. In very early Christian times Tertullian (160–225) wrote of fossils in mountains as demonstrating a time when the globe was overrun by water, although it is not clear whether or not he was talking about Noah's time. Both Chrysostom and Augustine thought of the Flood as being responsible for fossils, and Martin Luther was even more certain. Notwithstanding, there were two problems about the "flood theory":

1. Unknown and – as the knowledge of living animals and plants increased apace – presumably extinct organisms were found as fossils. The discovery of extinct organisms conflicted not so much with the Bible as with the theologians' "principle of plenitude", which held that God in the breadth of his mind had surely created any creature that was possible; and conversely God in his benevolence could not possibly permit any of his own creatures to become extinct. Plenitude was usually linked with the idea of the *scala naturae*, that there could be no gaps between forms in the chain. It also commonly involved an assumption of increasing perfection, more "soul", more consciousness, more ability to reason, or greater advance towards God. Extinctions were a problem for interpretation rather than a true conflict with scripture.

2. Information collected by an English surveyor, William Smith, and a French zoologist, Baron Cuvier, indicated that particular rock strata have distinctive fossils. Smith was involved in canal building and attempting to trace coal seams in mines, and he realised that geological strata could be identified by the fossils they contained. Such strata can sometimes be followed for hundreds of miles even when the rock formation changes. Smith developed these principles between 1791 and 1799, although his "stratigraphic map" of England and Wales was not published until 1815. During the same period French naturalists were actively collecting fossils in the limestone quarries around Paris, and Cuvier worked out the exact stratigraphy of these fossils (mainly mammals) in detail. The conclusion – unpalatable as it was at the time – was that there is a time sequence involved in the laying down of fossil-bearing strata, and that the lowest strata are the oldest. Later on it was possible to correlate strata, not only across England or Western

Europe, but between different parts of the world, if allowance was made for the same kind of regional differences which exist today in living faunas and floras.

At the end of the eighteenth century most geologists regarded the change between successive strata as the result of multiple catastrophes, the later forms being replacements specially made by the creator. The hangover from Plato's ideas about the impossibility of change prevented the fossil record being interpreted as a sequence of continuing changes, as it would be conventionally seen today.

The idea of evolution was in the air, as it were, during the second half of the eighteenth century. Maupertuis, Buffon, Diderot (Frenchmen), Rodig, Herder, Goethe and Kant (Germans) have all been claimed by historians of science as evolutionists, albeit without general support. They all postulated new origins (rather than a change in an existing type) or simple "unfolding" of imminent potential. Nevertheless, they are significant as being the immediate predecessors of Lamarck, who was the first to make a real break with the old, Plato-dominated world-view.

Lamarck (1744–1829)

Jean-Baptiste Lamarck was a protégé of Buffon, and from 1788 until his death worked in the French Natural History Museum. His key work was an evolutionary *Philosophie Zoologique* (1809), which he stated was needed to explain two phenomena:

1. The gradual increase in "perfection" from the simplest animals to man, seen simply in terms of complexity, and
2. The amazing diversity of organisms.

On these grounds, Lamarck claimed that one species may, over a longer period of time, become "transformed" into a new species; such evolutionary change solved the problems of extinctions. In doing this, he introduced a time factor, which has been described as the Achilles heel of natural theology: although a creator could design a perfect organism in an unchanging world, this would be impossible if the environment was changing, sometimes drastically. Adaptation to changes of climate, of the physical structure of the earth's surface, and of predators and competitors could only be maintained if organisms could adjust to the circumstances; in other words, if they could evolve.

Lamarck was a uniformitarian: he believed that the same factors had been operating on the earth from its beginning to the present time. This meant that he accepted that the earth was very old, with organisms changing constantly, albeit very slowly.

Furthermore, his studies in the Museum led him to believe that lineages did not only change in their own right, but that they also branched to produce separately evolving lines. The weakness in his ideas was in his suggestions about the mechanism whereby such transformations could come about. He believed there was a "natural law" which produced a trend towards greater complexity "from powers conferred by the 'supreme author of all things' . . . Could not this infinite power create an order of things which gave existence successively to all that we can see as well as to all that exists but that we do not see?" He also believed that individuals had a capacity to react to that environment, so as to remain in perfect harmony with it, although he did not state how newly acquired characters were supposed to be inherited. He simply asserted, "New needs which establish a necessity for some part really bring about the existence of that part as a result of efforts."

Although Lamarck prepared the way for Darwin in pointing to evidence that evolutionary change must have occurred, it is not true to claim that the two men's approaches or contributions were similar. Fifty years after Lamarck, Darwin wrote about *Philosophie Zoologique* that it was "veritable rubbish . . . I got not a fact or idea from it" although on another occasion he acknowledged: "The conclusions I am led to are not widely different from his [Lamarck's]; though the means of change are wholly so." The crucial difference between Lamarck and Darwin was that Lamarck believed the environment and its changes had priority, since these produced needs and activity for organisms, which in turn caused adaptational variation; Darwin began with the existence of variation in organisms, and the ordering action of the environment ("natural selection") followed.

From Lamarck to Darwin

However, before we reach Darwin, much more happened. Particularly significant was the attempted reconciliation of geology with Genesis. Superficially the two agreed in that human remains (the last act of creation) were apparently absent from the fossil record, and secondly that there seemed to be evidence of a Great Deluge covering the whole earth. Admittedly, there were difficulties in the latter. As early as 1681, Thomas Burnet calculated in *The Sacred Theory of the Earth* that eight times the volume of water in the present oceans would have been needed to cover all the land areas on earth. Burnet believed that all this water came from undersea caverns. Notwithstanding, by the eighteenth century the repeated changes in fossil faunas led to suggestions of a whole series of Floods.

In 1830, Charles Lyell published the first volume of his *Principles of Geology*, a book which had a great influence on Darwin. For Lyell, all geological processes were the results of secondary causes, i.e. they did not require supernatural interventions. He was a "uniformitarian" in contrast to subscribers to the prevailing "catastrophism", who assumed that God had repeatedly created new species after the recurrent catastrophes revealed in the fossil record. For most of his life Lyell was a firm opponent of evolution, although he was ultimately persuaded by Darwin.

Then in 1844 a book was published in London which

blasted the genteel debates of the time. It sold more than twice as many copies in the ten years after its publication as either Lyell's *Principles* or Darwin's *Origin*. *The Vestiges of the Natural History of Creation* was so heretical that the author took every precaution to remain anonymous; speculations about his identity ranged from Lyell or Darwin to Prince Albert, Queen Victoria's husband. Adam Sedgwick, Professor of Geology at Cambridge and Darwin's teacher, exploded with a review that stretched to eighty-five pages. He wrote to Lyell: "If the book is true, the labours of sober induction are in vain; religion is a lie, human law is a mass of folly, and a base injustice; morality is a moonshine; our labours for the black of Africa were works of madmen; and man and woman are only better beasts."

The author of the *Vestiges* was Robert Chambers, although this only became known after his death in 1871. He was a popular essayist and editor of *Chambers' Encyclopaedia*. He took an avowedly Christian stance: believing that when there is a choice between special creation and the operation of general laws instituted by the creator, "the latter is greatly preferable as it implies a far grander view of the divine power and dignity than the other". He had no doubt that the available fossil evidence showed that the fauna of the world had evolved through geological time, and, since there is nothing in inorganic nature "which may not be accounted for by the agency of the ordinary forces of nature", why not consider "the possibility of plants and animals having likewise been produced in a natural way".

What Chambers did was consistently to apply uniformitarianism to organic nature. The hierarchy of animals made no sense to him unless one adopted evolution. Like Darwin, he constantly emphasised how many phenomena, for instance rudimentary organs, could be explained as the product of evolution, whilst this made no sense in terms of special creation.

The trouble was that Chambers made many mistakes. He believed in spontaneous generation and backed up his belief by all sorts of folklore. He advocated no real mechanism whereby change might occur. He was savaged by his critics.

But he converted some influential people, including A. R. Wallace, the philosophers Herbert Spencer and Arthur Schopenhauer, and the poet Ralph Waldo Emerson. More importantly, he accustomed people to the idea of evolution; the critics of the *Vestiges* supplied the standard objections to evolution, which Darwin took care to answer in the *Origin*.

Darwin (1809–1882)

And so we come to Charles Darwin, younger son of a country doctor and one-time intending ordinand. It was Charles Darwin's *The Origin of Species by means of natural selection, or the preservation of favoured races in the struggle for life* (first published 1859, sixth and final edition 1872) that led to the general acceptance of evolutionary ideas by both the scientific and the general world. The reason for the immediate success of the *Origin* was Darwin's explanations for the distribution of animals and plants, and his convincing interpretation of the significance of vestigial organs. Other lines of evidence, from fossils, anatomical likenesses, and so on were well known to Darwin's contemporaries, but were explained away by them before an acceptable mechanism of evolution was available. In the longer term and much more important, it was Darwin's easily-understood *mechanism* of evolution which was his most important contribution. The need for a mechanism before a scientific idea is generally accepted also occurred with continental drift, which was put forward in detail by Wegener in 1915, but not commonly accepted until the nature of tectonic plates was described by geophysicists in the 1960s.

Darwin's doubts about the immutability of species arose from his study of geographical variation in both fossils and living forms during his time as naturalist on board the survey ship *Beagle* [1831–6]. For example he wrote in his journal about the Galapagos Islands that "I never dreamed that islands, about 50 or 60 miles apart, and most of them in sight of each other, formed of precisely the same rocks, placed under a quite similar climate, rising to nearly equal height, would be differently tenanted, but . . . I obtained sufficient materials to establish this most remarkable fact in the distribution of organic beings". Back in London, Darwin began in July 1837 to make notes on the transmutation of species. In 1838 he read "for amusement" Malthus's *Essay on the Principle of Population* and "being well prepared to appreciate the struggle for existence . . . it at once struck me that under these circumstances favourable variations would tend to be preserved, and unfavourable ones to be destroyed. The result of this would be the formation of new species. Here then I had at last got a theory by which to work."

Darwin wrote down his ideas for the first time in 1842, whilst on a brief visit to his in-laws (Josiah Wedgwood II, the potter) and his parents (in Shrewsbury). He expanded his 1842 sketch in 1844, and this latter version formed the basis of his first public pronouncement on the subject in 1858.

Darwin's original intention was to write a definitive book on evolution. However in the spring of 1858 he was sent by Alfred Russel Wallace an essay, *On the tendency of varieties to depart indefinitely from the original type*, written by Wallace whilst recovering from fever in the Moluccas. Darwin felt that this should be published, but on the urging of his friends Charles Lyell (whose *Principles* had first alerted Darwin to the reality of long-continued gradual geological change) and J. D. Hooker (son of the effective founder of Kew Botanic Gardens, and instigator of the study of plant geography), he allowed a revised version of his own 1844 essay to be forwarded with it to the Linnean Society.

Darwin's and Wallace's papers were read at a Linnean Society meeting on 1st July 1858, and published in the Society's *Journal* on the 20th August. They attracted little attention; the President of the Society declared in his report for 1858 that "The year which has passed . . . has not been marked by any of those striking discoveries which revolutionise the department of science on which they bear . . . A Bacon or a Newton, an Oersted or a Wheatstone, a Davy or a Daguerre, is an occasional phenomenon, whose existence and career seem to be specially appointed by Providence, for the purpose of effecting some great important change in the condition or pursuits of man." Controversy only broke out after the publication of the *Origin of Species* in the following year, and more vehemently after the confrontation between T. H. Huxley and "Soapy Sam" Wilberforce, Bishop of Oxford (inadequately briefed by Richard Owen, first Director of the Natural History Museum in South Kensington) at the British Association meeting in Oxford on 30th June 1860 (see p. 19).

The papers of both Darwin and Wallace clearly contain the three facts and two conclusions which are commonly taken as the simple summary of Darwinian evolution: the potential of all species to increase greatly in numbers, coupled with an approximate constancy of numbers, implies that there is a struggle for existence; and when variation is added to this, it is clear that natural selection must operate.

It was the ease with which these propositions could be understood that helped the fact of evolution to be generally accepted. In fact Darwin devoted more than half of the *Origin* to different lines of evidence that evolution had occurred: he had two chapters on the fossil record, two on geographical distributions, and one each on morphological likenesses (including comparative embryology, the interpretation of vestigial organs, and the meaning of classification), behaviour, and domestication. He devoted later books specifically to the origin of man and sexual selection, domestication, and adaptations in plants for pollination, insect-eating, and climbing. All these were parts of the book Darwin had originally intended to write before being forced into print by Wallace.

In chapters 6 and 7 of the *Origin* Darwin dealt with "difficulties" and "miscellaneous objections" to his theory. His main points concerned the nature of species and questions about the efficacy of selection. In a later chapter, he discussed the imperfections of the fossil record. Darwin knew that the maintenance of variation was a key weakness in his theory. The causes of variation are repeatedly referred to in the book and in later editions of the *Origin* he tended to accept that some Lamarckian explanation might be necessary (i.e. that the heredity of an individual might be affected by an environmental modification of its phenotype. No claim of Lamarckian inheritance by Kammerer, Lysenko, Steele, and many others over the years, has ever been substantiated). The problem was not resolved until the physical basis of heredity was discovered following the embryological conclusions of Weissman (1883) and the re-discovery of Mendel's work in 1900.

The issues faced by Darwin in the *Origin* are still raised today, and it is therefore relevant to summarise them.

Species transitions

If one species may evolve into another, why are forms linking two species not found? Darwin had to discuss this because of the hangover from Lamarckian speculation that existed when he was writing. Lamarck had suggested that evolutionary change comes from the use or disuse of organs and traits, so that transmutation arises from a varying response in an existing group. It would follow from this that there are no firm limits to any species, nor is a "natural" classification realistically possible since the evolving unit is the individual.

Darwin rejected this idea of species from his personal study of species in nature, and assumed a definition close to the modern one, that a species is an effectively isolated population or group of populations. He recognised that:

1. Closely related forms are likely to compete for the same resources, leading to the less-favoured one(s) becoming extinct. This has been shown repeatedly by experiment (perhaps most exhaustively in the flour-beetle *Tribolium*), with the important qualification that different varieties (or species) can survive together only where a heterogeneous environment allows different varieties to occupy different niches. However,

the key point is that one form will normally become extinct if a fitter form competes with it.

2. In a large area, different species replace each other geographically. In most cases these species seemed to have evolved in isolation and then expanded their ranges to come into contact. Geological changes (separating or connecting tracts of land) play a part, but at the level of present species the most important factor has been the Pleistocene, when previously widely-distributed forms were isolated in warmer or wetter refuges for relatively long periods, and changed sufficiently to remain distinct when the climate improved and they were able to re-occupy their former territory. Well-worked examples of this process are the Palaearctic ring of *Larus* gull species, and the *Heliconius* butterflies (and their mimics) in the Amazon basin. It is interesting that Darwin recognised the dynamic influence of historical events in forming new species, in contrast to the implicit assumption of both his contemporaries and many recent biologists that environments are stable and improbably homogeneous.

3. Transitional forms will almost certainly be less common than either the ancestral or descendent form, and hence liable to be overlooked or to become extinct. As collecting and the description of variation has progressed, it has been recognised that some species previously collected only from widely separated areas may in fact be connected by intermediate forms. We now recognise clines or different gradations of change in particular traits, and also that a species may be *polytypic*, i.e. may contain several geographically distinct forms which interbreed to a limited extent. Linnaeus confused matters by giving the name "variety" indiscriminately to geographical races, domesticated races, non-genetic variants, and inherited "sports". The idea of a polytypic species radically altered the Linnaean concept of a species: the older idea is of a species characterised by a gap

separating it from other groups, while a polytypic species is defined by actual or potential genetic continuity between allopatric, or geographically separated, populations. This does not, however, affect Darwin's point that forms in the process of change are likely to be uncommon. The discovery of active formation of new species (for example, *Drosophila* flies in Hawaii and cichlid fishes in Lake Victoria); the rarity of transitional forms; and the study of hybrid zones are throwing a great deal of light on the nature and integrity of species.

The effectiveness of natural selection

The most persistent criticism of Darwinism has always been that natural selection is merely a negative instrument removing inefficiency, but incapable of producing novelty or the seemingly perfect adaptation of such features as the eye of a mammal or bird, or the pattern of a butterfly's wing. We can deal with this under three headings:

1. *Cases of special difficulty* Darwin recognised three situations here:

   a. An organ (such as the wing of a bat) may be so specialised for its functions as to bear little resemblance to the prototype (the forelimb of a land-living insectivore) from which it must be presumed to have arisen. The difficulty is to envisage a series of organisms with organs of intermediate grades connecting these widely separated extremes.

   b. An organ of extreme perfection (such as the eye of higher vertebrates) may show such perfect and detailed adaptation that by comparison with the obstacles which the design of such an apparatus would present to human ingenuity, the mind is staggered by the effort of conceiving it as the product of so undirected a process as trial and error.

c. Some organs of seemingly trifling importance (such as the "fly-whisk" tail of the giraffe) are yet so clearly adapted to the function they perform that they cannot be regarded as accidental. In these cases it may be asked how such a trifling function can ever have been a matter of life and death to the organism, and so have determined its survival in the struggle for existence.

The first of these classes of objection applies to all evolution, whilst the second and third are difficulties more of imagination than of reason. It is impossible to deal with them in detail; R. A. Fisher has commented that "the cogency and wealth of illustration with which Darwin was able to deal with these cases was, perhaps, the largest factor in persuading biologists of the truth of his views". Here we can only note that:

i. *Function as well as structure evolves.* For example, there are organisms which have no image-forming eyes, but light sensitive cells. Any inherited variants which allowed detection of the direction of light, its size, movement, etc., could be of potential advantage, and subject to natural selection. The eye as we know it would be built up by the accumulation of many small steps, each of which could be adaptive. The result is efficiency in a particular environment, not perfection: one could envisage the human eye being "improved" by functioning better in poor light or under water, or failing to deteriorate with age; these attributes have never been "necessary" for human survival.

ii. *The usefulness (or "adaptive value") of a character can be tested by experiment.* Victorian biologists wasted a vast amount of effort speculating about the functions or value of particular organs; there is a similar tendency in the 1980s to pontificate about the significance of particular behaviour patterns. Apparently trivial traits may be shown to be highly important; it has only been recently shown that flies may seriously disturb tropical herbivores, and an efficient "fly-whisk" may add notably to fitness. Conversely other traits (even the horns of the Irish elk) may be incidental results of selection for other traits associated with growth.

The persistence of these criticisms has come from ignorance, often resulting from lack of research, rather than defects in the underlying ideas.

2. *The origin of novelty.* How can natural selection which functions to filter our deleterious variants lead to completely new developments? Is not natural selection limited to modifying existing adaptations? The answer is no, as consideration of three facts reveals:

    a. *All* traits are subject to variation.

    b. In evolution, novelty is introduced by a change in the environment: animals and plants invaded land because of an available habitat, not because it seemed a good idea. Some characters will be *pre-adapted* to the new environment.

    c. Even a very small selective advantage can lead to genetical change.

In the *Origin*, Darwin quoted Agassiz's work on echinoderms, showing how modification of spines may lead to the development of an apparently new and important trait, tube feet. Many similar examples are known. One of the major biological discoveries of the 1960s was the enormous amount of variation present in virtually every population, which means that a species can respond rapidly and precisely to new environmental stresses: bacteria can digest oil, aphids detoxify artificial poisons, and plants grow when introduced to the Antarctic Continent. There is no reason for believing that any reasonable novelties cannot occur in evolutionary time. Indeed even apparent disadvantages (such as sterile castes of insects) can evolve in appropriate conditions; natural selection is a mechanism for producing a priori improbable contingencies. (This fact incidentally answers claims that there has not been enough time for evolution to have taken place since the earth became habitable. The commonly used analogy that a monkey randomly typing will produce the works of Shakespeare,[1] but only if he had astronomical time, is irrelevant, since selection can rapidly and ruthlessly change the frequency of apparently random variation.)

3. *The strength of natural selection.* The power of natural selection to produce adaptation could only be illustrated by anecdote until quantitative methods of estimating fitness differences, rate and conditions of gene frequency change, and similar parameters became available. These were developed by R. A. Fisher, J. B. S. Haldane and Sewall Wright during the 1920s, and demonstrated the ability of selection differentials of less than 1% to bring about evolutionary change. The force of their theoretical arguments has been greatly strengthened with the discovery that selection pressures in nature commonly reach 10% or 20%.

Without condoning speculation by protagonists and opponents alike about the possible course of evolution, it can nevertheless be affirmed that answers given by Darwin to his critics in successive editions of the *Origin* have been repeatedly proved right by subsequent research.

Reaction to the *Origin*

I have devoted much space to describing the development of knowledge and scientific understanding of evolution in order to make two points:

---

[1] In his book *The Blind Watchmaker* Richard Dawkins shows how many of the conventional anti-evolutionary arguments can be demolished. One of his tests was to set his 11 month old daughter to work on a word processor (this was his equivalent for "a monkey randomly typing"), and then seeing how an intelligible sentence could be produced. He programmed the word processor to distinguish between "single-step" selection (where all the "right" answers have to turn up at the same time) and "cumulative" selection (where each improvement, however slight, is used as a basis for future building), and attained the intelligible sentence he was aiming for after only 64 generations.

The first is that the background to Darwin's work was an increasing knowledge of the natural world, particularly of the fossil record. It was this knowledge that forced a re-interpretation of the then current way of looking at nature.

My second point is that neither Darwin nor others who contributed to the "Darwinian revolution" were motivated by anti-religious ideals. Indeed many of the participants were devout Christians.

This is not the place to review in detail the reception of Darwin's ideas in the mid-nineteenth century. The aim of this book is to distinguish fact from interpretation, rather than recall history. In chapter 5 we shall examine recent criticisms of evolution, and how these fit into a scientific understanding of the natural world. For the present it is sufficient to make three observations:

(i) The furore following the publication of the *Origin* had more or less died down by 1870. In 1882 Darwin died and was buried in Westminster Abbey. The Christian estab-lishment gave its *imprimatur* when in 1884 Frederick Temple (later to become Archbishop of Canterbury) gave a series of lectures on the relations between religion and science, and argued that Darwin gave paradoxical sup-port for the traditional argument from design for the existence of God: "God did not make the things, we may say; no, but he made them make themselves."

(ii) Although there were exceptions, it was among orthodox believers with a firm hold on Calvin's doctrine of providence that the least nervousness about Darwin-ism was experienced. In the United States, three scien-tists who were evangelicals (James Dana, Asa Gray and George F. Wright) ensured that Darwin's ideas had a fair hearing; in denominational journals George Macloskie, a Presbyterian, and Alexander Winchell, a Methodist, argued their understanding of God and evolution; and distinguished evangelical theologians such as Warfield, Orr, A. A. Hodge, Iverach, Strong, Pope and McCosh all embraced the new biology.

(iii) The evolution debate had the misfortune to be part of several general debates going on in the mid-nineteenth century – on the impact of radical Bible criticism, working class defection from institutional religion, the separation of scientific authority from professional (usually clerical) scholarship. The "conflict" between science and religion was fostered by T. H. Huxley and the other Victorian scientists as a means to undermining the cultural leadership of the established church. Ironically, the "conflict" interpretation is also maintained by "creationists" who interpret the spread of evolution as a defeat for Bible authority (although, as we shall see, it is in fact only a defeat for a particular limited interpretation of the Bible). Few, if any, modern historians support this viewpoint.

Let the last word on the history of the evolution debate rest with Colin Russell, Professor of the History of Science at the Open University and a committed evangelical. He compares the cases of Darwin and Galileo:

It is profitable to do so because the dust has largely settled from the latter and because Galileo was persecuted by the Roman Catholic Church. Also no one (cranks apart) has any doubt today about the correctness of a heliocentric hypothesis for the solar system; so we may feel a little more detached and objective. Yet having said that I must now insist that on all the main theological issues the Darwinian case is virtually a re-run of the Galileoan. It makes no more sense to assert a literal rendering of Genesis 1 than it does of Psalm 19: 4–6 or Joshua 10: 1–14 (both of which passages were taken to justify a geocentric universe). That this was no real problem to many Christians of the seventeenth century should not surprise us. A long tradition back to at least Augustine accepted that the Holy Spirit "accommodated" himself to the language of ordinary people, expressing spiritual truths in homely language. Calvin and the Reformers found no problems here. Nor did Galileo who ironically observed that the scriptures were given us "not to show how the heavens go but how to go to Heaven". One wonders whether the minority of Christians who get upset by Darwin had even heard of Galileo, and, if so, whose side they would have been on.

Russell brings together history, the interpretation of history, Scripture, and the understanding of scripture. It is now timely to move to what is the most important part of this book for Christians: Bible teaching about creation.

3

The Bible account

[God] has made everything beautiful in its time. He has also set eternity in the hearts of men; yet they cannot fathom what God has done from beginning to end.
Ecclesiastes 3:11

The Genesis accounts of Creation are about the Creator first and foremost; they are only secondarily about His actions. It is God who speaks; it is God who sees His work is good; and it is God who puts His image into man. The author of Revelation sums up the position from the other end, as it were, of the Bible:

> You are worthy, our Lord and God,
> to receive glory and honour and power,
> for you created all things,
> and by your will they were created and have their being.
> [Revelations 4:11]

The Westminster Confession makes the same point: "God created the world for the manifestation of the glory of His eternal power, wisdom and goodness." Calvin described creation as the theatre of God's glory.

Creation was not necessary. God did not "have to" create the world. "The God who made the world and everything in it . . . does not live in shrines made by man, nor is he served by human hands, as though he needed anything, since he himself gives to all men life and breath and everything" [Acts 17:24, 25]. Both the world and man originate from the free and sovereign will of God. From the point of view of creation, the Creator is in every respect independent of his creatures. This distinguishes the Creator of the Bible completely from any pantheistic ideas which say that the living world represents parts of expressions of God, "for from him and through him and to him are all things."

The first three chapters of Genesis set the scene for the rest of the Bible, teaching about the nature of God and the impact of evil on the creation. We are presented with the outline of a great range of divine truths – about relationships with God and with each other, and about responsible behaviour. In theological language, Genesis 1–3 is a "theodicy", stating and justifying God's goodness in an evil world. These are all basic facts. The problem we have to face is how to translate the language of these chapters for the 1980s: are we faced with a literal description of God walking around on earth, and the Devil in the form of a talking snake; or ought we to take into account other knowledge we have about the world and ourselves? This means that we have to be extremely careful about our *interpretation* of these chapters; our prime concern must be what God is trying to say to us. Four general points are relevant:

1. The Genesis 1 and 2 accounts are different from each other, but complementary rather than contradictory. Von Rad [1963] sees them as "in many respects open to each other", and argues that exegesis should be carried out on both of them together. The second story is in many respects a recapitulation and sequel to the first account and provides an introduction to chapter 3. Whatever the literary history of the two accounts, in both there is one supreme God, by whose act and word order was established out of chaos, and upon whom man is dependent for his existence and place in the order of created beings; both emphasise obedience to God and fellowship with him; and both introduce

ideas integral to the whole of the Old Testament. In his Tyndale commentary, Kidner [1967] underlines this: in chapters 2 and 3 "man is the pivot of the story (while) in chapter 1 he was the climax. Everything is told in terms of him; even the primaeval waste is shown awaiting him [2:5b] and the narrative works outwards from man himself to man's environment (garden, trees, river, beasts and birds) in logical as against chronological order, to reveal the world as we are meant to see it: a place expressly designed for our delight and discipline. It is misleading to call this a second creation account, for it hastens to localise the scene, passing straight from the world at large to 'a garden in the east'; all that follows is played out on this narrow stage."

2. The Bible creator is distinct from those portrayed in other Middle East mythologies:

a. He is presented as a living God, unmistakably personal. The verbs of Genesis 1 express an energy of mind, will and judgement which excludes all question of God being "it" rather than "Thou".

b. He is the only God, the creator and sovereign of all that is. The world is separate from him, not an emanation or expression. A Jesuit writer, Robert Faricy [1982: 2,3], expresses this as the "de-devinisation" of nature: "Genesis underlines that creatures are in no way divine . . . They are merely creatures, not divine, infinitely distant from their ineffably transcendent Creator, and completely subject to him as their Lord . . . Behind the earth's fertility, and causing it, we do not find the sun or the moon, or, as in many myths, the tree of life. We find only the creative word of God. Nature is radically distinct from God."

c. His ways are perfect. The series of explosions and cataclysms in Genesis declare that heaven can make no truce with sin, whether it is the Godward sin of unbelief and presumption (as in Eden and Babel), or the manward wrongs of violence, lust and treachery. The Bible God is utterly different from the creator in other widespread myths. There is an Egyptian account dated c.2350 BC which describes the act of the god Atum who brought forth gods on a primaeval hill above the waters of Chaos. Atum "who came into being by himself" next brought the world into order and out of the dark deep assigned places and functions to the other deities. Another myth describes mankind as being created from the fears of the sungod Ra, all men being created equal in opportunity to enjoy the basic necessities of life. However, the best-known of the creation-myths is a Babylonian adaptation of a Sumerian cosmogony known as *Enuma Elish*. This begins with two gods Tiamat and Apsu, but then other gods were born, and Apsu tried to do away with them because of their noise. However, one of them, Ea, managed to kill Apsu; then Tiamat, bent on revenge, was killed by Ea's son Marduk. Marduk used the two halves of Tiamat to create the firmament of heaven and earth. He then set in order the stars, sun, and moon, and lastly, with the help of Ea, created mankind from clay mingled with the blood of Kingu, the rebel god who had led Tiamat's forces.

Throughout the ancient Near East there was a conception of a primary watery emptiness and darkness, with creation a divine act *ex nihilo* (i.e. out of nothing) and man made for the service of the gods. But the Old Testament account stands distinct with its clarity and monotheism; in it are no struggles between deities to exalt any particular city or race. The contrasts between Genesis 1 and all the known extra-biblical cosmogonies are more striking than the resemblances.

3. The Bible creation narratives must not be read as a *scientific* account. They are concerned with theological truths. This is not to impute factual inaccuracy, but to insist upon the purpose of the passages. In mediaeval

times, verses such as Psalm 19:5, 6 and 96:10 were used to support the idea of a fixed earth, surrounded by a moving sun and stars; as we have seen, Galileo was persecuted on the basis of this interpretation. We now accept that these texts are teaching about God not astronomy. Likewise, we must beware of reading biology into the creation narratives when their primary aim is theological. Writing from an avowed "creationist" standpoint, Cameron [1983] has argued that Genesis 1–3 is a theodicy, and all attempts to harmonise scriptural and secular language must fail because they are irrelevant.

Francis Schaeffer [1973: 35, 36] has warned that "We must remember the purpose of the Bible: It is God's message to fallen men . . . The Bible is *not* a scientific textbook if by that one means that its purpose is to give us exhaustive truth or that scientific fact is its central theme and purpose. Therefore, we must be careful when we say we know the flow of history: we must not claim, on the one hand, that science is unnecessary or meaningless, nor, on the other hand, that the extensions we make from Scripture are absolutely accurate or that these extensions have the same validity as the statements of Scripture itself."

Douglas Spanner [1965] has summarised the Bible teaching as "not that God made an elegant mechanism (like a super-clock) and then retired to a distance to watch it perform according to built-in laws; but rather that he remains immanent in His creation, personally energising on a moment-to-moment basis all its multifarious happenings. He 'makes grass grow' [Ps. 104:14], 'make the hinds to calve' [Ps. 29:9], and 'sends rain' [Matt. 5:45] (note the present tenses). It is in this way that the Bible accounts for the regularity of nature, which we loosely express by saying that similar causes always produce similar effects. This regularity is not due to the perfection of a mechanism, but to the faithfulness of God."

4. The most persistent misapprehension about God and creation, however, is that knowledge of causal mechanism automatically excludes any possibility that God is acting in a particular situation. "Creationists" seem to assume that if evolution is acknowledged to occur, then God cannot be the Creator. As we saw in chapter 1, this assumption is nonsense. Notwithstanding, the relation between God and mechanism is a key question.[1]

As an aside it is worth noting that very rarely in Scripture is there any indication of the method God used to achieve his purpose. One exception is Exodus 14:21–22, where we read "all that night the Lord drove the sea back with a strong east wind, and turned it into dry land. The waters were divided, and the Israelites went through the sea on dry ground . . ." The actual site of the Israelite crossing is uncertain, but at the traditional place, near the northern end of the Gulf of Suez, the water has been blown "back" several times in recorded history. The prevailing wind in Egypt is from the west, and an east wind is very unusual. Thus God's intervention in this case, although certainly providential, involved natural processes. Notwithstanding, it was truly a miracle. It involved a disturbance of the normal pattern of events by God in such a way as to draw attention to himself; the miracle lay in the place and timing of a physical event, not merely in the fact of its occurrence.

The mechanisms producing the plagues of Egypt are not given in the Bible, but all of them could have perfectly reasonable natural causes: deposits from upstream lakes not infrequently stain the Nile floodwaters a dark reddish-brown colour similar to blood; they stir up flagellates toxic to fish; prolonged flooding

---

[1] This raises the general question of miracles. In this section I deal with some of the characteristics of God's action, but only in the context of the chapter. An article I wrote in *Nature* describing the nature of miracles and scientists' attitudes to them is reprinted as an Appendix to this book (pp. 165–72).

can lead (and has done so) to enormous numbers of frogs and biting insects; flies often transmit epidemic diseases of domestic animals ("all the cattle of the Egyptians died"); locusts and sand-storms ("darkness") are common in the Near East. In situations like this it is fairly easy to suggest how God might have worked. The point of the story is not simply to state God's control over the natural world – that is implicit throughout Scripture and is one of the main inferences from the creation accounts in Genesis – but to emphasise his care for his own people and his response to specific prayer.

In most cases, we know no apparent mechanism for particular miracles. For example, it is not clear why the Jordan should be more effective in healing leprosy than "Abana and Pharpar, the rivers of Damascus" [2 Kings 5:12], or why Christ used a mud ball to rub the eyes of a blind man [John 9:6]. If a modern pathologist had been present at any of the healing miracles he could in principle have described the changes that took place in the diseased cells of the sufferer as they became healthy, although he would not have been able to say *why* the changes were taking place. Whether we are able to say anything or nothing about the way a miracle was brought about is irrelevant to the purpose of the miracle, and does not affect or detract from the sovereignty of God. A causal explanation is usually on a different level from an explanation which describes divine activity.

It is sometimes asserted that by definition a miracle must happen instantaneously, and in particular that the *fiat* framework of Genesis ("God said . . . let there be . . . and God saw that it was good") shows that the creation miracles have no time element. This assumption involves a confusion: God is outside time, so it is irrelevant to apply our time-scales to Him. From the human point of view it is clear that miracles may take some of our time to complete their effect. A particularly clear example of this is Christ's healing of the blind

man recorded in Mark 8:23–5, when sight was restored gradually ("when he had spat on the man's eyes
. . . [the man] looked up and said, 'I see people; they
look like trees walking around'. . . . Once more Jesus
put his hands on the man's eyes. Then his eyes were
opened, his sight was restored, he saw everything
clearly"). Another example is the feeding of the
Israelites in the wilderness – manna was provided
every day.

The question of time from the point of view of creation is
highlighted by the Hebrew word *bara*, which is commonly
taken to refer to a special act of God in creation, in
distinction to the word more commonly used in the
creation narrative, which has the implication of moulding
existing material (in the way that a potter moulds clay:
Jeremiah 18:3–6). In Genesis 1, *bara* is used to describe the
origin of matter [verse 1], animal life [verse 21], and man
[verse 27; see also 5:1]. It is used in Isaiah 42:5 in a similar
way ("God the Lord . . . who created the heavens") while in
Isaiah 43:1 it refers to the chosen people, a miraculous work
which had taken centuries ("this is what the Lord says – he
who created you, O Jacob"). Psalm 19 and other great
psalms of worship of the creation marvel at the regularities
of nature (which science assumes and describes), just
as much as the things that are irregular. In other words,
the "everyday" processes of God are just as much his
handiwork and his creation as the unusual and un-
expected things he does. It is therefore inconsistent to insist
that the world used for creation in Genesis I necessarily
means something without process; conversely, we cannot
argue as a matter of principle that an event which uses
a known process (such as evolution by natural selection)
is *necessarily* less the work of God than an event that did
not.

This brings us back to the connection between God
and creation. Perhaps the best way of regarding divine
creation and biological evolution is to understand them

as complementary explanations. The God of the Bible is primarily a creative upholder [Colossians 1:17], and only secondarily a divine watchmaker. There is no conflict or rivalry in distinguishing between *why* God created (which is described in the Bible) and the methods or mechanisms used, which are the business of science to probe. Francis Schaeffer [1973: 27] has described how his approach to Genesis 1 changed as he reflected on God's relationship to his creation: "As a younger Christian, I never thought it right to use the word *creation* for an artist's work. I reserved it for God's initial work alone. But I have come to realise that this was a mistake, because while there is indeed a difference there is a very important parallel. The artist conceives in his thought-world and then he brings forth into the external world . . . And it is exactly the same with God. God who existed before had a plan, and he created and caused these things to become objective." In other words, we must distinguish between *why* God created (which is described in the Bible) and the objective *cause*, which is the role of science. The fact that God created all matter and life, and did not merely shape it, is important. It is implicit in some of the ideas of the previous two sections. Prior to the action of God "in the beginning" [Genesis 1:1] there was no other kind of existence than God.

This means that matter is not eternal, and that there is no other power in existence in the universe outside His control. It indicates also, as we have already seen, that God is distinct from His creation, which is not merely an external manifestation of an Absolute. There are several strands of evidence for the doctrine in the Bible.

1. There is no mention of any pre-existing material out of which the world was made. Nor do the Scriptures ever represent the world as an emanation from God by a necessity of His nature.
2. The descriptions of primary creation rule out any idea of mere formation. "God said . . ." is the language of Genesis; and in Psalm 33:6 we read "By the word of the Lord were the heavens made."

3. The same doctrine is involved in the absolute dependence of all things on God and in His absolute sovereignty over them. Thus Ezra addressed God, "You are the Lord, you alone, You made the heavens, even the highest heavens, and all their starry host, the earth and all that is on it, the seas and all that is in them. You give life to everything" [Nehemiah 9:6; see also Colossians 1:16, 17; Revelation 4:11]. Everything other than God is said to owe its existence to His will.

4. The author of Hebrews begins his illustration of the nature and power of faith by referring to creation as the great fundamental truth of all religion [Hebrews 11:3]. If there is no creation, there is no God; conversely creation as a divine act is a fact which we know only by revelation.

5. The doctrine of creation derives from the infinite perfection of God. There can be only one infinite being. If anything exists independently of His will, God is thereby limited. The God of the Bible is an extra-terrestrial God existing outside of and before the world, independent of it, its creator, preserver and governor. The doctrine of creation is a necessary consequence of theism. Hence the doctrine is presented on the first page of the Bible as the foundation of all subsequent revelations about the nature of God and His relation to the world, and from the beginning one day in seven is appointed to be a perpetual commemoration of the fact that God created the heaven and the earth.

Biblical interpretation

When we turn to the actual Genesis text itself, we find two accounts of creation which are utterly different to the accounts which would appear in a modern book. Blocher [1984] points out how crucial our approach is, because the celebration of God's creation as a work of six days followed by a day of sacred rest is undoubtedly intended to be an allusion to the Sabbath [Exodus 16:29, 20:8–11, etc.].

Blocher asks "what is the meaning of the allusion? And how are we to compare the assertion of the seven days with the billions of years, at the lowest estimate, which current scientific theory attributes to the origin of the universe? It is impossible to avoid these questions, which revolve round the central question, that of interpretation: how are we to understand Genesis when it enumerates the days of the divine handiwork?"

There are five ways of interpreting the "days" of Genesis 1:

1. *Literally*: The traditional interpretation is, of course, that the days represent a literal twenty-four hour period. Defenders of this view treat the Genesis account as history, arguing that the text contains no indication of figurative language; they maintain that those who take any other view have given in to the spirit and mind of an apostate world. They quote other parts of the Bible as apparently treating the Genesis story in the same way – verses such as Exodus 31:14 (the Sabbath commandment), Matthew 19:4 (Jesus' comment on the relation of man and woman), and 2 Peter 3:5 (the reminder that the earth was formed out of water). However, the latter two passages are not relevant and it is not clear that they imply a literal reading. Even the Exodus passage does not require a literal interpretation of "day"; it merely refers back to Genesis, and in the repetition of the sabbath law [Exodus 31:17], clear use of an anthropomorphism is made, when the text says that "the Lord . . . rested". The second version of the Ten Commandments [Deuteronomy 5: 12–5] replaces the reference to creation with the memory of Israel's slavery in Egypt, which does not contradict Exodus 20, but warns of too close a link between the work of the Creator and the weekly rhythm of human life.

   It is clearly possible to interpret the Genesis 1 "day" as a twenty-four hour period, but it is hard to maintain that no other interpretation is legitimate, and dubious to reject all the scientific evidence about the age of the earth (the weight to be given to this is considered in chapter 5).

2. *The Gap Theory*: The Scottish divine, Thomas Chalmers, seems to have been the first person to suggest that the six days were days of reconstruction, not of creation. He argued that a catastrophe happened between the creation of the heavens and the earth [Genesis 1:1] and the formless and empty earth described in Genesis 1:2. Indeed, there could have been several catastrophes, corresponding to the mass extinctions revealed in the fossil record. The days of reconstruction would have no connection with either the original creation or the fossil record, and therefore (it is argued) there can be no conflict with science. This "gap theory" was incorporated by Scofield into his "annotated Bible" and achieved wide circulation. However, it is exegetically unsound. It depends on Genesis 1:2 reading "the earth *became*", which is inadmissible. Also it requires the verb translated "make" in Genesis 1 (and Genesis 2:2, Exodus 20:11) to have the meaning "remake". There is no justification at all for this.

3. *Days of Revelation*: P. J. Wiseman has argued strongly (*Creation Revealed in Six Days*, 1948) that, since the "Sabbath was made for man" [Mark 2:27] (clearly the Creator did not need a day's rest), it was intended for human rest, "then it is only reasonable to suppose that what was done on the 'six days' also had to do with man; and if with man, then obviously on the six days God was not creating the earth and all life, because man was not in the world when these were being created". Wiseman then goes on to suggest that the implication of the repeated phrase "God said" was that it means that God said to man what He had done in times past; the six days of Genesis 1 therefore become days of revelation. However like the Gap

Theory, this idea fails on exegetical grounds, because the word translated "made" in Exodus 20:11 cannot mean "made known".

4. *The Concordist Theory*: The suggestion that the days of Genesis represent geological epochs has already been mentioned. It is commonly propounded. For example Ellicott's conservative evangelical *Commentary* (1897) is explicit that:

> A creative day is not a period of twenty-four hours, but an *aeon*, or period of indefinite duration, as the Bible itself teaches us . . . By the common consent of commentators, the seventh day, or day of God's rest, is that age in which we are not living. So in Zechariah 14:7 the whole Gospel dispensation is called 'one day'; and constantly in Hebrew, as probably in all languages, *day* is used in a very indefinite manner, as for example in Deuteronomy 9:11 (AV, RSV).

While not going along with Ellicott in accepting that the seventh day is necessarily the Gospel age, it is certainly true that the Hebrew world *yôm* does not always mean a twenty-four hour period in the Old Testament: it may be a time of special divine activity ("day of the Lord" – Isaiah 2:12), an indefinite period ("day of temptation" – Psalm 95:8), or simply a long period (Psalm 90:4). In Genesis 2:4, the word used for the whole span of time during which God was creating is the same as the one used for a single day in Genesis 1. Probably most apologists would agree that it is not particularly meaningful to speak of a twenty-four hour day in terms of an eternal God who is outside time.

The difficulty with the Concordist Theory arises when the details of the fossil and scriptural records are matched with each other. Although there is considerable agreement between the order of events, there are discrepancies. For example trees (Day 3) precede marine organisms (Day 5), and birds (Day 5) precede terrestrial animals (Day 6), contrary to scientific expectation. But the biggest disagreement is the creation of the sun and stars on the fourth day after that of dry land and its vegetation on Day 3. The usual explanation of this is that on Day 4 God dispersed a thick covering of cloud, so that the sun and moon and stars were revealed to earth for the first time. The snag here is, as with the Gap Theory, that advocates of a particular view would like to change the meaning of a simple word; in this case, to change "make" in verse 15 to "reveal". There is no justification for this; there is a perfectly good word in Hebrew for "appear", which is used in verse 9.

5. *The Literary Interpretation*: The idea that the Genesis "days" represent a framework for the creation account rather than an indication of time sets it apart from the other four interpretations. It was embraced by Augustine, who believed the six days were "a sextuple confrontation of the angelic nature with the *order* of creation". It is held by respected modern evangelical commentators, such as J. A. Thompson in the *New Bible Dictionary*, who affirms that "the whole (of Genesis 1) is poetic, and does not yield to close scientific correlations". E. F. Kevan, formerly Principal of the London Bible College, in the first edition of the *New Bible Commentary* says:

> The biblical record of creation is to be regarded as a picturesque narrative, affording a graphic representation of these things which could not be understood if described with the formal precision of science. It is in this pictorial style that the divine wisdom in the inspiration of the writing is so signally exhibited. Only a record presented in this way could have met the needs of all time.

In the second edition of the *New Bible Commentary*, Meredith Kline wrote:

> The prologue's (Genesis 1:1–2:3) literary character limits its use for constructing scientific models, for

its language is that of simple observation and a poetic quality, reflected in the strophic structure, permeates the style. Exegesis indicates that the scheme of the creation week itself is a poetic figure and that the several pictures of creation history are set within the six work-day frames not chronologically but topically. In distinguishing simple description and poetic figure from what is definitely conceptual the only ultimate guide, here as always, is comparison with the rest of Scripture.

Francis Schaeffer [in *Genesis in Space and Time*, 1973: 124] goes even further when he discusses time in the early chapters of Genesis. He points out that time is not used chronologically in these chapters, nor are genealogies complete or even in the expected order. He is emphatic in his conclusion:

> In regard to the use of the Hebrew word *day* in Genesis 1, it is not that we have to accept the concept of the long periods of time that modern science postulates, but rather that there are no clearly defined terms upon which at this time to base a final debate . . . Prior to the time of Abraham, there is no possible way to date the history of what we find in Scripture.

Henri Blocher has described the literary interpretation and its attractions well. I am grateful for permission to quote his words at length:

> The literary interpretation takes the form of the week attributed to the work of creation to be an artistic arrangement, a modest example of anthropomorphism that is not to be taken literally. The author's intention, is not to supply us with a chronology of origins. It is possible that the logical order he has chosen coincides broadly with the actual sequence of the facts of cosmogony; but that

does not interest him. He wishes to bring out certain themes and provide a theology of the sabbath. The text is composed as the author meditates on the finished work, so that we may understand how the creation is related to God and what is its significance for mankind.

This hypothesis overcomes a number of problems that plagued the commentators. It recognises ordinary days but takes them in the context of one large figurative whole; the differences in order between the two "tablets" (i.e. Genesis 1 and Genesis 2) no longer cause difficulties, neither does the delay in the creation of the stars, nor does the confrontation with the scientific vision of the most distant past. So great is the advantage, and for some the relief, that it could constitute a temptation. We must not espouse the theory on the grounds of its convenience but only if the text leads us in that direction.

To put it plainly, both the genre and the style of the Genesis 1 prologue provide strong grounds for presuming in favour of the literary interpretation. We admire its author as a wise man, supremely able in the art of arranging material and very fond of manipulating numbers, particularly the number seven. From such a writer the plain, straightforward meaning, as in two-dimensional prose, would be most surprising when he is setting out the pattern of seven days. From such a writer you would expect the sort of method which is discerned by the "artistic" interpretation.

Immediately we pass to the study of the days themselves, we find once again that the author keeps closely to his most careful style. He shows the same geometrical mastery and thus suggests that other thoughts overshadowed in his mind any concern for chronology. Two centuries ago Herder recognised the powerful symmetry between the two triads of days: Day 1 corresponds to Day 4, Day

2 to Day 5, Day 3 to Day 6. Corresponding to the light (1) are the luminaries (4); to the creation of the expanse of the sky and the separation of the waters (2) correspond the birds and the fish (5); and to the appearance of the dry land and of vegetation (3) correspond the land animals including mankind together with the gift of food (6). Medieval tradition had recognised the broad pattern, since it distinguished the work of *separation* (Days 1–3) from the work of *adornment* (Days 4–6). It would be better to speak first of *spaces* demarcated by divine acts of separation, then of their corresponding *peopling*. It can also be stressed that only the creatures of the second series are mobile (some speak of the immobile creatures for Days 1–3 and of mobile creatures for the rest). The duality of habitations and inhabitants reappears in Isaiah 45:18. It is tempting to play on the plausible nuances of *tōhû* and *bōhû* in the second verse and find there a negative foretoken of the two themes: indeed, the separating work of the first three days deals with the trackless, shapeless desert and the work of the three following days fills the *bōhû*, the void. At any rate the thought behind the two is most carefully distinguished at the conclusion, in 2:1: "Thus *the heavens and the earth* were finished (Days 1–3), and *all the host of them* (i.e. the great crowds of all that filled the heavens and the earth)". Let us notice a further point of composition. The presence of two works in parallel manner on the third and sixth days, far from betraying a difficulty for the author, is in our opinion, as in Barth's, a mark of his skill. The second work in some respect anticipates what is to follow, prevents the series of three closing in on itself and thus consolidates the structure of the week. Thus the vegetation on Day 3, although an element of the immobile environment, is already, at the same time, one of the first inhabitants; in the text the power of reproduction relates it to the

animals and thus it announces the second series. On Day 6, mankind created in the image of God is the creature who will enjoy the sabbath rest. As we shall see, his privilege of bearing the divine image has basically the same meaning as the ceasing from work on the seventh day. Thus between the final two days there is no separation. The structure of our hymn-narrative leaves nothing to chance; it is the fruit of mature meditation.

The reader who is in sympathy with that meditation no longer stumbles at the "problem" of the fourth day with its "delayed" creation of the stars. He has no need to construct the problematic theory of days like solar days but without the sun, of which the text gives not the slightest hint. If the principle which directs the distribution of the works is their classification into two categories, the places and their occupants, then the creation of the luminaries is in its proper, logical position. Chronology has no place here. [*In the Beginning*, pp. 50–2]

Blocher sums up the possible interpretations of "day" firmly in favour of the last choice: "The theological treasures of the framework of the Genesis days come most clearly to light by means of the 'literary' interpretation. The writer has given us a masterly elaboration of a fitting, restrained anthropomorphic vision, in order to convey a whole complex of deeply meditated ideas."

The question remains of course, whether the creation of the world was *in fact* sudden or gradual, but we are in error if we insist *in principle* that creation in six days of twenty-four hours is any more consistent with God's nature and his supernatural power than creation over a long space of time. The conclusion from a detailed inspection of the Genesis "days" is that Genesis 1 does not state or deny either possibility. It is only if we look at such facts as we can discover from examining the world that we have to accept that things are not as they were when the world was first created: in the past there were very large reptiles (dinosaurs) and now there are none; there used to be vast forests made up of kinds of trees and ferns that do not now exist (except fossilised as coal beds); new volcanic islands have appeared; river valleys have been deepened; and so on. The changes are due to processes of some kind or another, even if they have operated faster in earlier times than now, and even if they involved catastrophic events like a great flood. In other words, it is difficult to avoid the conclusion that God has used at least some natural processes to bring the world into its present state. We must retain open minds about the speed and time of his methods if we are to be faithful to Scripture.

Progression

The main discontinuities in the creation story are the divisions between the days; if the passage was not expressed in this way, it would read like a continuous creative progression from simple inorganic substance to man made in the image of God. As we have seen, ascertaining the correct meaning of the "days" is far from siimple. However, there is stronger ground for arguing another sort of gap in the progression of creation, and that is the special intervention of God in the creation of matter, animal life and man. The word used of God's activity in these contexts is *bara* (create) [1:1, 21, 27 twice, also 2:3, 4]. On other occasions the word *asah* (to make) is used. We have already noted the significance of *bara* (p. 53), but it is worth re-emphasising the use of *bara* and *asah* in Genesis 1. God is invariably the subject of the verb *bara* in the Old Testament [e.g. Isaiah 40:26; 45:7, 8], and the word emphasises a special divine action, in contrast to *asah* which has more the sense of "modelling" with pre-existing material (like a potter making a pot). Hence it seems legitimate to suggest that God created in a distinct way when he made matter, animal life and man. All creation is a divine activity, but there seem to be grounds for insisting that these events may have been occasions for "special creation" as opposed to "divine creation through natural processes".

4

Man and woman

Man's fate is like that of the animals; the same fate awaits them both. As one dies, so dies the other. All have the same breath. All go to the same place, all come from the dust, and to dust all return. Who knows if the spirit of man rises upward and if the spirit of the animal goes down into the earth?

Ecclesiastes 3:19–21

So far, we have referred to the creation of the human race only in passing, but in many ways the nature of humankind is central to Christian debates about evolution. Put crudely, is man an ape "on the way up", or is he (and she) a special creation separated from the rest of the animal creation by divine act? If we are still improving, then the necessity for grace or redemption becomes less important; if we are "made in God's image" and share in Adam's sin [Romans 5:12] then evolutionary processes are apparently impossible.

The key factor in understanding our nature as taught in the Bible is to examine the meaning of the "image of God" which distinguishes us from the other animals: "God created man in his own image . . . God formed man from . . . the dust of the earth and breathed into his nostrils the breath of life, and man became a living being" [Genesis 1:27, 2:7].

Because Christ was God, and took upon himself the form

of a man, it is easy to fall into the trap of assuming that God's image is the same thing as our human form. A moment's reflection shows the naïvety of this: the Bible refers to God as having anatomical parts (eye, arm, etc; even wings: Psalm 36:7, etc.), but only when it describes an activity or function. The idea of God's image in us being the same as our physical body is as far-fetched as the scholastic belief that God resided in the pineal gland (largely on the basis that no function was known for it in mediaeval times).

At one time, theologians tended to equate God's image or spirit in man with rationality. There is no scriptural support for this, and studies on animals show that they can be regarded as capable of rational thought and learning in just the same way as we are, albeit to a lesser extent. Indeed it is difficult to identify absolute differences between the minds of animals and man: animals are capable of some degree of aesthetic appreciation and abstract thought; they can have "nervous breakdowns"; they may "play" elaborate games; and show considerable community and family care. W. H. Thorpe, one of the most distinguished animal behaviourists, quotes six levels of mental activity described by Hobhouse [1913] of which four could be discerned in animals, while the remaining two were regarded as characteristic of man. Hobhouse called these two "the correlation of universals" and "the correlation of governing principles". They involve a recognition of abstract moral law or, in Thorpe's [1961] words, "eternal values which are in themselves good . . . of course we can find in the higher social animals, such as wolves, behaviour which appears altruistic, unselfish, indeed 'moral'. Nevertheless I believe at this level we can see a difference between the minds of humans and of present-day animals, and that in Hobhouse's last two categories we have reached a distinction which we can for the time being at least regard as fundamental."

Modern theological opinion is similarly united in agreeing that the *imago dei* is non-anatomical; theologians regard God's image as a relational, not a physical entity [Blocher, 1984]. For example, Emil Brunner [1939], commenting on 2 Corinthians 3:18, noted that "man's meaning and his intrinsic worth do not reside in himself but in the One who stands 'over against' him . . . Man's distinctiveness is not based upon the power of his muscles or the acuteness of his sense-organs, but upon the fact that he participates in the life of God, God's thought, and God's will, through the word of God". C. F. D. Moule [1964] concluded, "The most satisfying of the many interpretations, both ancient and modern of the image of God in man is that which sees it as basically responsibility [Ecclesiastes 17:1–4]." H. D. MacDonald [1981] has proposed that "image should be taken as indicating 'sonship' which holds together both the ontological and relational aspects of the image".

Genesis 2:7 describes human creation as a two-stage process: the physical form was moulded by God from pre-existing material (which he had, of course, earlier made himself), and *then* He "breathed into his nostrils the breath of life and man became a living being". To quote again the comment of Calvin on the verse, man is linked with the natural creation by his body being made of the same substance as the rest of creation, and distinguished through being "endued with a soul, whence it received vital motion; and on the soul he engraved his own image, to which immortality is annexed". In other words, we are a special creation in our human-ness, and this human-ness is not located in any specific physical part of us. We acknowledge this distinction in our evangelism, when we proclaim that our response to God has to be a response of the will, unconstrained by experience, family background or inherited capabilities [John 1:13]. Although our spiritual nature resides in a physical body, it is not the same thing [1 Corinthians 15:42ff].

Fossil man

Once we accept that our spiritual nature is not the same thing as our bodily envelope, our physical ancestry and genetic relationships fall into perspective. *Homo sapiens* has one of the best fossil records of any animal species, despite the criticisms that can legitimately be made of the over-enthusiasm of palaeoanthropologists. The earliest accepted remains of fossil *Homo* (assigned to the species *H. erectus* and found widely distributed in the upper Pleistocene about a million years ago) had a skeleton not unlike our own, but with a smaller brain; well-developed ridges of bone over the eyes; a ridge on the back of the skull to attach powerful neck muscles, a sloping forehead; flat face with no chin; and large upper incisors. Nevertheless, *H. erectus* was an erect walker, a meat eater and toolmaker (belonging to the Acheulian or great hand-axe culture); physically and (in a loose sense) culturally, he was not very different from "true" man. He was also quite closely related to the australopithecine "near-men" of Africa. Although palaeontologists differ about the details of the relationships between apes and possible human ancestors, there is no dissension about the general outline of primate history. The fossil evidence of relationships is supported by an enormous amount of anatomical, physiological and genetical evidence. For example the chromosomes of humans and the other great apes are almost identical, the main difference being the fusion of two ape chromosomes to form a single element in man; the "genetic codes" of the DNA of chimpanzee and man differ by less than two per cent.

Notwithstanding our close genetic relationships to other animals, these studies are not relevant to our understanding of man *if* our distinctiveness as humans is strictly speaking spiritual rather than physical. Pearce [1969] has made a strong case for the biblical Adam being a neolithic farmer, cultivating his patch on the slopes of the Turkish plateau as climatic conditions improved following the final retreat of the Pleistocene ice-sheet. This would place him about 10,000 years ago, of the same order as Archbishop Ussher's dating from biblical chronology of 6,000 years ago.

The evidence for this is what Pearce calls "a type of cultural zone fossil" in Genesis 2–4:

1. "The Lord God took the man and put him in the garden of Eden to work it and take care of it" (2:15). The particular connection of Adam and Eden with tillage – agriculture – is mentioned three times. In the "neolithic revolution" man was able to control his food supply for the first time, which made possible – indeed required – a settled existence.

2. Domestication spread rapidly from its believed origin in the Near East to many parts of temperate Eurasia (11:9).

3. A settled existence led to the possibility and need for markets and services – in other words for towns. Among the earliest of these was Catal Huyuk, on the Turkish plateau (4:17).

4. The main diagnostic clue to Adam's culture was that he cultivated crops and bred animals. Early in the record the beginning of metal-working (iron) is noted (4:22).

5. Primitive farming is, in modern terminology, labour-intensive. The neolithic revolution permitted and gave rise to the first rapid increase (and hence diversification of occupations) in the human population. Hence the emphasis in patriarchal times on massive reproduction (1:28a) and large families.

6. The climate at the end of the ice-age was dry and the initial vegetation would have been tundra (2:5), with localised glacial rivers (2:6), forming oases which probably attracted animals (2:19b). The Garden of Eden is placed (2:10–14) in the region where prehistorians have found the first traces of the neolithic revolution (both archaeological and botanical). The word translated "Eden" could be the same as the Babylonian "Edinnu" meaning a plateau or steppes. The land which lies east of the upper reaches of the Tigris was known by the Kassites as Cush, implying that the Gihon was the Araxes and that Eden was in the region assigned to it by Sumerian tradition, at the head water of the great river of Mesopotamia. The cool evenings of 3:8 would be typical of the high plateau.

It is fully consonant with Genesis that God created Adam in the body of a Near Eastern farmer in comparatively recent times in archaeological terms. If we accept this, the term "man" as used by the palaeontologist or anthropologist is a much wider term than "man" as used in the Bible (the existence of pre-Adamic men conveniently explains such old "chestnuts" as where Cain got his wife from, and who were the "Nephilim", Genesis 6:4). However, it is worth recording a comment by B. B. Warfield that "it is to theology as such, a matter of entire indifference how long man has existed on earth".

The Fall

The inherent problem about Darwinian man "evolving upwards" from the apes is that he (and she) should be getting better all the time, morally as well as physically. This contrasts with the scriptural position that we are a special creation, inbreathed by God at a specific point in time.

Was there a single historical Adam and a single historical Eve? Paul's teaching seems to demand this [Romans 5:12, 17; 1 Corinthians 15:21, 45]. The doctrine clearly rests on the fact that "sin entered the world through one man, and death through sin". Three points need making:

1. The death that came into the world was spiritual (separation from God), not physical death. Adam and Eve "died" *the day* they disobeyed (Genesis 2:17) but they survived physically (and produced all their family) after their exclusion from God's presence.

2. By the time neolithic farming was beginning in the Middle East, *Homo sapiens* had spread to many parts of the world: there were Indians in America, Aborigines in Australia, and so on. A neolithic Adam and Eve could not be the physical ancestors to the whole human species. But we have already seen that physical relationships are irrelevant where God's human creation is concerned: spiritual inbreathing and

"spiritual death" are not determined by or spread through Mendelian genes: they depend upon God's distinctive methods of transmission. As Kidner [1967:30] has pointed out:

> with one possible exception[1] the unity of mankind "in Adam", and our common status as sinners through his offence are expressed in scripture not in terms of heredity [Isaiah 43:27] but simply of solidarity. We nowhere find applied to us any argument from physical descent such as that of Hebrews 7:9, 10 (where Levi shares in Abraham's act though being "still in the loins of his ancestor"). Rather Adam's sin is shown to have implicated all men because he was the federal head of humanity, somewhat as in Christ's death "one died for all, therefore all died" [2 Corinthians 5:14] . . . After the special creation of the first human pair clinched the fact that there is no natural bridge from animal to man, God may have now conferred his image on Adam's collaterals to bring them into the same realm of being. Adam's "federal" leadship of humanity extended, if that was the case, outwards to his contemporaries as well as onwards to his offspring, and his disobedience disinherited both alike.

The Bible insists on the spiritual unity of the human race [Acts 17:26; Romans 5:12–14]. This does not necessarily mean a genetical unity, even though this would be the simplest interpretation.

There is an old idea originally proposed by Weidenreich that the various races of mankind are of different antiquity, i.e. that some races are more primitive than others. The evidence for this sugges-tion is largely zoogeographical – that is, based on the

---

[1] Genesis 3:20, naming Eve as "mother of all the living". However the concern of the verse is principally to reiterate in the context of death, the promise of salvation through "her seed" (Genesis 3:15).

distribution of races around the world – and has little anthropological support. From the present point of view its truth is immaterial: no one seriously doubts that the species *Homo sapiens* (as distinct from the races of mankind) has a single origin.

More interestingly, recent work on the distribution of biochemical variants can most easily be interpreted to mean that man has been through a "bottleneck" in numbers during his recent evolutionary past. The reasons for this are technical. They are based on the frequencies of inherited variants of proteins, particularly haemoglobin. These demand that during the past million years, the human species comprised a single pair for one generation, or an effective population of 10,000 for half a million years, or something in between. This assumes that the variants considered are selectively neutral, which is only partly true. Nevertheless it is strong circumstantial evidence that man has passed through an "Adam and Eve" situation in the early history of species (long before neolithic times) [Jones & Rouhani, 1986].

3. The New Testament passage which most explicitly refers to the Fall is Romans 8:18–23. This clearly teaches that the whole of creation (including man) has been affected by the presence of sin in the world. However, a closer examination shows that the Fall primarily involved man, and only secondarily and consequentially the rest of creation.

The danger of Romans 8:18–23 is trying to understand it out of its context. It is, in fact, part of the theme of redemption and the Spirit's work which occupies Paul from chapters five to eight of the letter; the passage about the Fall and suffering links with Romans 5:3–5, where suffering and hope are associated with the gift of the Spirit.

Now the Fall resulted in death [Genesis 2:17; Romans 6:23], that is, separation from God. This had two consequences: the relationship of "love and cherish" between Adam and Eve became one of "desire and domination" [Genesis 3:16, 4:7]; and "tending" in Eden became "toil" outside [Genesis 3:18, c.f. Leviticus 26:3ff; Proverbs 24:30–34]. Romans 8:20 states that the frustration currently experienced by creation is not innate in it, but was a consequence of "the will of the one who subjected it". Whether this was God or Adam does not matter; the point is that the frustration arises because of an extrinsic event, and can be dealt with by faith, as Paul pointed out in Romans 5:2. C. F. D. Moule paraphrases Romans 8:20: "For creation was subjected to frustration, not by its own choice but because of Adam's sin which pulled down nature with it, since God had created Adam to be in close connexion with nature." The teaching of the whole of this central section of Romans is how Christ overcame death (on the cross), and how the consequences of this are dealt with, contrasting life in the flesh with life in the Spirit [Romans 6:13]. In Romans 8:19 Paul writes about the "sons of God" who are to be revealed; in the same passage he defines "sons of God" as "those who are led by the Spirit of God" [8:14]. The next verse [8:20] describes the vanity and frustration which results from a failure to respond to the Spirit. As Kidner says, "leaderless, the choir of creation can only grind in discord". The whole of the Book of Ecclesiastes is a commentary on this verse.

The message of Romans 8:18–23 is thus one of hope – hope not looking to the distant future but to the time when the redeemed accept their reunion with God, and therefore their responsibility for nature. Paul's argument is that as long as man refuses (or is unable through sin) to play the role God created for him, the world of nature is dislocated and frustrated. Since man is God's vice-gerent on earth (which is part, at least, of the meaning of being "in God's image"), he has inevitably failed in his stewardship from the moment he first disobeyed God and dislocated the relationship. Some Christians interpret any facts which they find morally difficult as the "results of the Fall" (such as "nature red in tooth and claw", or the enormous number of human foetuses which spontaneously miscarry). We must be clear that these are complete guesses; we are almost completely ignorant about the moral state of affairs before the Fall (although we know that there were land-slides and extensive floods on earth before man, and that many dinosaurs suffered from arthritis). It is hazardous to argue from such apocalyptic passages as Isaiah 11:5–9 ("the wolf will live with the lamb") that particular ecological conditions were God's primary purpose. Moule [1964] has commented on the Isaiah verses:

> no one with a grain of sense believes that the passage is intended literally, as though the digestive system of a carnivore were going to be transformed into that of a herbivore. What blasphemous injury would be done to great poetry and true mythology by laying such solemnly prosaic hands upon it! . . . Indeed it would be a catastrophic dislocation of the whole of ecology if the lion did begin to eat straw like the ox, or for that matter if the microscopic defenders within the body gave up attacking the invaders which cause disease.

Woman

Eve was formed from Adam's side [Genesis 2:21]. In his *Man: Ape or Image* [1981], John Rendle-Short says "This must be historical truth or myth . . . It is naive to dismiss the story of Eve as myth and assume no violence has been done to Scripture. At least seven doctrines of fundamental importance to the whole human race, but especially to Christians, are directly founded on the fact that Eve was created out of Adam" [p. 39].

This comment betrays a failure by Rendle-Short to recognise that God may communicate by other means than historical events, just as Jesus taught by parables as well as by miracles. If God is truly omnipotent, clearly he *could* have made Eve from one of Adam's ribs, but that does not mean that he actually did so. Modern man has the same number of ribs as modern woman. The emphasis of the account is on the similarity of the man and the woman, on their close kinship, and on their possession of an identical essence. And as Blocher [1984:99] says:

> The presence of one or several word-plays casts doubt on any literal intention on the author's part; they reveal an author who is in no way naive, but who uses naive language for calculated effects. Paul's *ek* (where he states in 1 Corinthians 11:8 that woman was made (*ek*) from man) does not require a literal interpretation of Genesis on this point. There are different kinds of causality, and that which the apostle has in mind may be exemplary or final. It could perfectly well be said that the woman is "from" (*ek*) the man if he played the part of a prototype and if God created the woman because of the need that man had of her. Such a conclusion emerges by itself from Genesis 2, even if the text does not reveal the detailed method of the divine procedure. The author plays on the double meaning for rib, which also means "side" and therefore *"alter ego"*. Arabs use the expression "He is my rib" to mean "He is my close friend". We use a similar turn of phrase when referring to one's "better half". If Paul does not require a literal reading, and if the word for rib/side is rich in symbolism, we have the right to consider the hypothesis of figurative language.
>
> Certain other clues favour it. A second word-play may be involved in the word rib/side. In Sumerian, *ti* means both "rib" and "life". Now the name Eve comes from the word for "life" [Genesis 3:21]. The image of the rib removed and transformed had also the great advantage of throwing into relief the traditional phrase, "bone of my bones and flesh of my flesh". And there are no end of possibilities of allied symbolical

inferences which have given ingenious commentators a field day. One fairly misogynous rabbinic commentator puts these words into God's mouth: "Where shall I make her from? Not from the head, lest she stand too proudly; nor from the eyes, lest she be excessively curious; nor from the ears, for she would risk being indiscreet; nor from the nape of the neck, which would only encourage pride . . ." and so it goes on. The rib is selected in order to make the woman modest – but the dreaded faults will appear all the same. The old commentator Matthew Henry, who seems to follow Thomas Aquinas, is in much closer agreement with the spirit of Genesis: God did not make the woman "out of his head to rule over him, nor out of his feet to be trampled upon by him, but out of his side to be equal with him, under his arm to be protected, and near his heart to be beloved". More subtly, Augustine understood that the man is the strength of the woman (from him comes the *bone*), whilst the woman softens the man (in the place of the rib, God closes up the *flesh*). There is no question of attributing *all* these meanings to the inspired author's intention; but he no doubt had several of them in mind, which increases the probability that the writing is figurative.

Genetic determinism

At this point we must digress to consider the morality described in Romans 1:18 (and which is linked with the idea of "conscience"). Darwin realised there was an enormous difficulty about the evolution of morality. In the *Descent of Man* [1871], he wrote:

It is extremely doubtful, whether the offspring of the more sympathetic and benevolent parents, or of those who were the most faithful to their comrades, would be reared in greater numbers than the children of selfish and treacherous parents belonging to the same tribe. He who was ready to sacrifice his life, as many a savage has been, rather than betray his comrades, would often leave no offspring to inherit his noble nature. The bravest men, who were always wishing to come to the front in war, and who freely risked their lives for others, would on average perish in larger numbers than other men. Therefore it hardly seems probable that the number of men gifted with such virtues, or the standard of their excellence, could be increased through natural selection, that is by survival of the fittest.

This problem exists only if moral traits are inherited in a similar way to height or eye colour, and this derives from a common but mistaken belief that *all* our characteristics are determined by the genes we inherit from our parents. Aldous Huxley must bear some of the blame for this assumption: in *Brave New World* he spelt out the Darwinian nightmare of selecting (or condemning) people of different genetic make-up to particular occupations. Such determinism seemed to be confirmed by the discovery that simply inherited chemical defects can cause gross mental retardation (phenylketonuria was the first such to be recognised); that Down's syndrome is caused most commonly by the presence of an extra chromosome; and that men with two Y chromosomes (instead of the normal one) are often aggressive criminals. However, this assumption of genetic determinism has been over-stressed in the popular mind; genes only predispose us to certain characteristics or behaviour, and their expression can very often be modified by changing the environmental conditions. For example, phenylketonurics fed from birth on a phenylalanine-free diet can grow up to be virtually normal; many – perhaps most men – with an extra Y chromosome have perfectly normal behaviour. Notwithstanding there is a persistent belief that we are dependent on our genes for our failures (and sometimes for our successes). There are repeated claims that certain behaviours (such as homosexuality) are not morally culpable, because they are inherited; these claims are completely unjustified.

The link between genes and behaviour received considerable publicity following the publication of *Sociobiology* [1975] by E. O. Wilson, a Harvard entomologist. Wilson based his arguments on a point made fifty years earlier by J. B. S. Haldane, that if the unselfishness (even to the point of self-sacrifice) of an individual had an inherited basis and if he (or she) supported near relatives so that they raised more children than they would otherwise have done, then the altruism genes would be selected and spread in the same way as (for example) inherited resistance to a disease. This concept was formalised as "inclusive fitness" by W. D. Hamilton in 1964, and by John Maynard Smith in the same year as "kin selection", the name by which the idea has become known. The 1950s and 1960s saw much interest in biology and behaviour, expressed in the writings of Konrad Lorenz, Niko Tinbergen, Wynne-Edwards, Robert Ardrey, and Desmond Morris, and in such television series as David Attenborough's *Life on Earth*. In his book, Wilson reviewed the evolution of social behaviour in many animal groups, and in a concluding chapter extrapolated his conclusions to man, claiming that sociobiology (defined as "an interdisciplinary science which lies between the fields of biology (particularly ecology and physiology) and psychology and sociology") is the key to understanding human behaviour.

Wilson has been attacked by both sociologists and socialists, who see his ideas as disruptive to their dreams of improving society by manipulating the environment. However, his suggestions have been attractive to those seeking a naturalistic explanation of human altruism. For example, Peter Singer [1981] has written, "Sociobiology . . . enables us to see ethics as a mode of human reasoning which develops in a group context . . . so ethics loses its air of mystery. Its principles are not laws written up in Heaven. Nor are they absolute truths about the universe, known by intuition. The principles of ethics come from our own nature as social reasoning beings."

This is not the place to argue the correctness or otherwise of sociobiological claims for man. The arguments turn on the relative importance of the factors which control human behaviour. What is relevant here is to recognise that this debate can be conducted entirely on the scientific level, without Christians having to take up positions. Singer is wholly wrong to claim that sociobiology can replace (or control) ethics; if we have an *imago dei* (which we accept or reject by faith, not by proof in the scientific sense), then our behaviour is affected by it, even though we may have an entirely naturalistic explanation for the behaviour in terms of human history and natural selection. The debate is exactly the same as the one that took place in the eighteenth and nineteenth centuries when it was realised that our physiological processes are analogous to those of a machine, or in the 1930s and 1940s when the brain was seen to have similarities to a computer. The fallacy is to assume that we are "nothing but" a machine, a computer, or a programmed genetic reaction; we are these, but we are also human beings made in the image of God.

A generation ago, William Sargant [1957] discussed the signs that often followed John Wesley's preaching, and maintained that the conversions associated with the preaching were spurious, because the signs could be mimicked by physiological or pharmacological techniques. This claim was as mistaken as that of Singer: it assumed that any event can only have one description, and that knowing a causal mechanism excludes the intervention or control of God.

There are three possible views about human origins: as "nothing but" a highly evolved ape; as "nothing but" a special creation of God made complete in every respect; or as an ape inbreathed by God's spirit, with an evolutionary history and a unique relationship with the creator. The important point to recognise is that only the last viewpoint allows us to resolve the paradox of our altruistic behaviour and accept the logical validity of scientific investigation of our nature.

Darwin and man

The only place that Darwin refers in the *Origin of Species* to the evolution of man is near the end where he wrote that "In the future I see open fields for far more important researches . . . Much light will be thrown on the origin of man and his history." He was, of course, aware of the heat that would be generated by the application of his ideas to man. Passions had been aroused by Robert Chambers's *Vestiges of Creation*, and Darwin did not want the scientific debate about evolution confused.

However, early and influential support for Darwin's ideas came from Charles Lyell. Ever since his geology had first opened up the question of the origin of species, Lyell had been disturbed at the prospect of degrading man through a link with animals. But in the *Antiquity of Man*, Lyell [1863] accepted the archaeological evidence for the existence of primitive "sub-humans" and had to face the prospect of human evolution. He admitted the plausibility of Darwin's conclusions, and was even prepared to accept a gradual progress through the history of life – something he had been arguing against for decades. Where he balked was the appearance of man as a continuous development from his closest animal relatives; he believed that the distinctive qualities of humans must have been produced by a sudden leap in organisation, taking life to a new and higher plane. Alfred Russel Wallace, co-discoverer of natural selection with Darwin, came to a similar conclusion. This led him to a belief that we possess a soul capable of existing independently of the body, and he became a spiritualist. In his Bampton Lectures referred to earlier (p. 43), Frederick Temple believed that the "enormous gap" separating human from animal nature might have been due to a "spiritual faculty . . . implanted by a direct creative act".

Ironically, these early post-*Origin* interpretations of man were obscured by the scientific arguments about natural selection in the first generation of this century. The rediscovery of Mendel's work in 1900 and the realisation that genetic mutation formed the raw material for evolution produced a rift between biometricians and palaeontologists on the one hand, and geneticists on the other. During the 1920s the long-continued gradual evolutionary progressions revealed by the study of fossils evoked theories of intrinsic evolutionary urges, linked with pantheistic notions of *élan vital* and "emergent evolution". Alfred North Whitehead [1929] suggested that the world is best seen not as a collection of distinct objects, but a complex of on-going processes in which nothing is ever isolated from the rest of nature. But these speculations are part of the on-going scientific debates about evolution. They are described in chapter 5.

5

Evolution and science

A time to search and a time to give up . . . a time to be silent and a time to speak.

Ecclesiastes 3:6,7

It is not the purpose of this book to describe evolution in the same way as in a scientific textbook. However, there is so much misapprehension and misinformed criticism about evolutionary mechanism that it seems worthwhile to review briefly the status and problems of evolution from the time of Darwin to the present day. This is necessary for anyone wanting to make up his own mind about evolutionary questions, but it is also required for an understanding of the attacks on evolution by "creationists", which we will consider in chapter 6.

There have been three main periods of debate about evolution: in the early 1900s; during the 1920s and 1930s, leading to the neo-Darwinian synthesis; and in the 1960s and 1970s.

1900s

Biometricians and Mendelians

Darwin had no doubt that inherited variations were extremely common. He had been convinced of this by his observation of varieties in nature, but more especially by his contacts with practical animal breeders and horticulturists. On the other hand, he knew nothing about the mechanism of inheritance. He accepted the conclusions of the botanists Kölreuter (1733–1850) and Gärtner (1771–1850) who crossed a vast number of plant varieties. Their repeated finding was that the characteristics of both parents blended in the offspring, which tended to be intermediate between the parents. This meant that if a new variant arose, it would have only half its expression in its offspring, one quarter in the grandchildren (because it would almost certainly have to cross with the non-variant form), and so on. New variation would have to arise at a high rate if it was going to persist long enough to be operated on by selection.

In *The Variation of Plants and Animals under Domestication* (1868), Darwin put forward his "provisional hypothesis of pangenesis" in an attempt to account for this. He suggested that each part of an organism produces "free and minute atoms of their contents, this is gemmules" which pass to their reproductive organs and are thence passed to the next generation. "Direct and indirect" influences of the "conditions of life" (as suggested by Lamarck) could in this way become part of the hereditary constitution of the organism; as he wrestled with the problem, Darwin found himself more and more adopting Lamarckian ideas.

Meanwhile the search for a better understanding of the genetical process led in 1900 to the rediscovery of Gregor Mendel's work (originally published in Brno, Czechoslovakia in 1866) by de Vries in Holland, von Tschermak in Austria, and Correns in Germany. Mendel's main conclusions (the regular segregation and independent assortment of inherited traits) were soon confirmed in animals by Bateson and Punnett in Cambridge and Cuénot in Paris.

The application of Mendelian ideas had two important consequences for evolutionary ideas: they indicated that inherited factors did not blend, but persisted unchanged through the generations, thus removing the chronic problem of variation loss; and they appeared to show that inherited variation was discontinuous. However, a group of biometricians (i.e. those who measure biological material) who had been studying the consequence of continuous variation for evolution came to regard Mendelism as irrelevant to evolutionary change. The six years following the rediscovery of Mendelism witnessed increasingly bitter confrontations between Mendelians and biometricians over mutation theory, the meaning of genetical dominance, etc.

The physical basis of heredity was not generally accepted until the work of T. H. Morgan and his colleagues on sex determination, linkage, and mutation in *Drosophila melanogaster* connected breeding results with cytological knowledge (summarised in *The Mechanism of Mendelian Heredity* published in 1915). However, Mendel's "laws" (Mendel himself did not state any laws, but his conclusions are most easily summarised in this way) were everywhere being confirmed, and the Mendelians increasingly gained the upper hand. The biometric-Mendelian controversy degenerated into personal conflict, and ended when Weldon, one of the chief biometricians, died of pneumonia at the age of 46, but the split between the supporters of continuous and discontinous evolution continued to grow, and was only resolved in the 1930s.

1920s and 1930s

Palaeontologists and geneticists

In the early 1900s, the importance of natural selection in evolutionary change came to be regarded as of little importance; the emphasis was increasingly laid on the origin of variation rather than on its maintenance. Huxley and Bateson believed that continuous variations were too small to generate significant selection pressures; Galton (Darwin's cousin and a founder of the study of human genetics) believed that the selection of continuous variations soon reached a limit because of the counteracting effect of regression. A Danish botanist, Wilhelm Johannsen, showed (1903) that selection for weight within pure (i.e. self-fertilised) lines of beans had no effect, and concluded from this that continuous variation was not inherited and therefore unimportant in evolution. (The significance of the fact that different lines produced beans of different mean weight was not realised at the time, although it is the aspect of Johannsen's work which is almost always quoted nowadays.)

The mutation theory of Hugo de Vries (one of Mendel's rediscoverers) was particularly influential at this time. De Vries worked with the Evening Primrose, *Oenothera lamarckiana* and observed frequent mutations in his stocks. He argued that evolution depended on such mutations, and that species originated by "jumps" or saltations rather than the accumulation of small differences as suggested by Darwin. We now know that de Vries's *Oenothera* mutations were mostly due to chromosomal rearrangements, together with the segregation of recessive traits, and are not mutations in the modern sense. Notwithstanding, a generation of biologists grew up convinced that evolution was "driven" by mutation with natural selection taking a minor role.

Meanwhile palaeontologists were building up an increasingly confident picture of evolutionary changes in fossil strata. It seemed clear that much change was continuous and progressive; evolutionary "jumps" did not exist when the record was continuous over long periods. The mutations being studied by laboratory geneticists appeared to have nothing in common with real evolution. Darwin's own emphasis on gradual evolution was continued by the palaeontologists, via the biometricians.

During the 1920s the gap between palaeontologists and geneticists widened. As knowledge of mutations *sensu stricto* increased, it seemed that they almost invariably produced deleterious traits which were inherited as recessives, whereas adaptively useful traits were virtually always dominant. It is no wonder that this period led to a widespread disenchantment with classical Darwinism, and the propounding of a variety of other theories of evolutionary mechanisms: Berg's *Nomogenesis*, Willis's *Age and Area*, Smut's *Holism*, Driesch's *entelechy*, and others. None of these was satisfactory, and all depended upon an almost mystical inner urge (or *élan vital*) for their functioning. It is unfortunate that three standard and still-read histories of biology (by Nordenskiold, Radl, and Singer) were written during this time, and the idea that evolutionary theory is an illogical mess has been perpetuated.

This impasse persisted for over thirty years. Natural selection was seen by many of the early geneticists, particularly Morgan and Goldschmidt, as an entirely negative process which served merely to eliminate unfit deviations. Genetics apparently had nothing to say about the nature of gaps between species, the origin of evolutionary novelty, the formation of higher (that is, supra-specific) categories, or the integrated nature of evolutionary change. In the 1920s the palaeontologist, Osborn, and the taxonomist, Rensch, both distinguished evolution by mutation (that is, by discontinous jumps) from evolution by speciation (that is, by gradual, continuous genetic change). In 1932, Morgan went so far as to assert that "natural selection does not play the role of a creative principle in evolution".

Then within twelve years (1936–47) scientists who had previously held different views about evolution came to a common mind. This event became known as the "neo-Darwinian synthesis"; it was largely summarised in Julian Huxley's *Evolution: the Modern Synthesis*, published in 1942. It was not the result of one "side" being proved right, and the others wrong; but in Ernst Mayr's words, "of an exchange of the most viable components of the previously competing research traditions". It involved three steps:

1. *The removal of objections to the compatibility of Darwinian evolutionary theory and Mendelian genetics*, largely through an increase in understanding of the inheritance of continuous variation; and the demonstration that the two sets of ideas were complementary. This

came mainly through the work of the geneticists Fisher, Haldane and Wright.

2. *The recasting of these ideas in terms of populations rather than "types"*, thus taking account of the existence of variation and the wrongness of the classical, static notion of species, dating back to Plato.

3. *The recognition that ideas coming from a range of disciplines require these concepts for their own development*. This was realised independently by specialists working in their own disciplines: Simpson in palaeontology, Rensch and Mayr in biogeography and systematics, Huxley in zoology, Waddington in embryology, Stebbins in botany, and so on.

This is not the place to analyse the factors that brought the synthesis into being. Suffice it to say that the main element was a better understanding of the nature and maintenance of variation in populations. A key element was Fisher's hypothesis of the evolution of dominance, in which he argued (and was soon backed up by experimental evidence from Ford, Harland and others) that mutant genes are not inevitably deleterious and recessive, but that genetical dominance arises through natural selection of modifying genes which increase the expression of advantageous traits (and in the same way recessivity is produced by selection for a reduced expression of deleterious traits). This is a complicated notion involving a recognition that the possession of a gene is not the same thing as the manifestation of the trait determined by that gene, and that genes interact to produce characters which are subject to natural selection. It shows how wrong is the oft-repeated statement that virtually all mutations are detrimental to their carriers.

The importance of the neo-Darwinian synthesis is that it re-established the unity of biology which Darwin's ideas had originally provided, and thus made possible generalisations within an otherwise impossible diversity of living organisms. The Periodic Table gives a similar service to chemistry. It is this unifying element which apparently makes evolution into something more than a simple scientific theory, and allows such diverse topics as fossil sequences, gene frequency changes and polymorphism, extinctions, adaptation, and so on, to be brought within a single umbrella. There may be disagreement about the inter-action or relative importance of particular mechanisms, but there is no viable scientific alternative to Darwinian evolution for understanding nature. This is a strong claim, but it is why biologists tend to be unimpressed with the philosophical (or for that matter, "creationist") criticisms discussed below. Evolutionists are as willing as any scholars to discuss the correctness of their interpretation of particular data, but at the same time they tend to dismiss apparent difficulties as trivial; this is not a consequence of being brainwashed, but a sober judgement on order in the whole world of biology.

Before leaving the neo-Darwinism synthesis, two scientific points and one theological are worth making.

The first is that a small but significant proportion of newly-arisen mutations are advantageous to their carriers. Concern about the genetic effects of radiation has led to an enor-mous amount of research into the effects of new mutation. This has shown conclusively that some mutants are favour-able, and in experiments where new mutations are induced at a high rate by radiation or chemicals, these may virtually offset the effect of the majority of mutants which are unfavourable.

Secondly, mutations are random in their occurrence, but evolutionary change is directed in its occurrence. Individuals do not receive virtually identical sets of genes from their two parents, but slightly different versions of approximately one in ten of all genes. This means that if the environment changes, there is a considerable amount of variation available for selection; in other words, adaptive change does not have to wait for rare new mutations but can use existing variation. Examples where this has been shown include genes conferring resistance to insecticides in mos-quitoes or tolerance to heavy metal pollution in grasses, which are present in low frequencies in most populations, and enable rapid response to new selection pressures if the environment changes.

In this context, it is worth making the point that "randomness", as used of a scientific event, is nothing more than a confession of ignorance. Early statements that mutations are completely "random" in their occurrence and effect have had to be considerably modified by a growing understanding of cell biology and chemistry so that the probability of a particular change in a gene can now be expressed fairly accurately. However, randomness is a term which can be used only of events occurring in time. A Christian who believes that God is both creator and sustainer of the world [Colossians 1:16–17] but also outside the space-time fabric of it, must necessarily accept also that He is in some sense in control of all mutational events.

For the ordinary man in the street, the apparent purposelessness of the raw materials of evolution is one of the most significant factors convincing him that there cannot be a God of order in control of the world, leading to a pessimism eloquently expressed by Monod in his book *Chance and Necessity* [1970]. In contrast, no committed Christian should be prepared to admit that even such a random event as a road accident is necessarily outside God's purposes for him or her. It is therefore especially important for the Christian to recognise and witness that there is no conflict in accepting a world which seems to be full of evidences of design and one in which functional adaptation derives from random mutation; we can assert the former by faith (Hebrews 11:3), but for those able to understand, it is possible to strengthen and exercise faith by discovering other processes by which the world has come to be.

The third point is that natural selection is a process brought into being by God. A common anti-evolution argument is that nature "red in tooth and claw" is an effect of the Fall. In fact this is a humanist argument against God, asserting that no loving God would create such a world as the one that we live in. Our reply is that the present situation is not as God originally intended it to be, but we have to be careful lest we imply that the evil in nature was therefore created by the devil. This cannot be so: the devil is not a creator. The order of the world is affected by the Fall and the curse of God, but God is still the creator and the sustainer of all that is, and there is no lesser god or devil who is either a creator or upholder. It was God himself who subjected the creation to futility [Romans 8:20]. The processes we see in nature are God's processes, even if they are processes set up to deal with a fallen world rather than a perfect world. Natural selection is a divine institution in just the same way as the State is a divine institution, or as it was the Father's will for his Son to suffer [Luke 22:42; 24:26. See also 1 Peter 4:19, etc.]. We assume God will work in a particular way; when he chooses another, we are surprised. Animals do eat one another, and we are even told lions seek their prey from God and God gives it to them [Psalms 104:21, 27].

We must face the fact that this is how the world is, and not try to escape by talking about an ideal world created at the beginning. Indeed, if we are to be honest, we know extremely little from Scripture about the biology of the pre-Fall world, although one thing we do know is that plants and seeds were given to man for food, which means that those plants and seeds must have died in the biological sense. The "death" introduced by the Fall [Romans 5:12] must be distinct from the biological death present before Adam's sin.

1960s and 1970s

Neutralism and selection

There is a recurring argument that evolution cannot depend upon mutation, because mutations are "always harmful". This is a false argument. Although most mutations are harmful to their possessors, since there are random changes in a functioning organism, some are undoubtedly beneficial. There are now many examples of this in natural populations, as well as in laboratory experiments (see p. 88).

Mutations provide the raw materials for evolutionary change, and it is necessary that their effects be fully examined. This was attempted during the 1950s and 1960s when the achievements of the neo-Darwinian synthesis were formalised in theoretical arguments, in particular by H. J. Muller (one of T. H. Morgan's colleagues in *Drosophila* research) and J. B. S. Haldane. Muller reasoned that there is an upper limit to the amount of variation that may be carried by an individual or population. We all have a burden of deleterious genes produced by recurring mutation; these form a genetic "load" bearing us down. Clearly there is a limit to the number of such genes which any individual can carry and still survive to reproduce. In so far as these genes reduce health and fertility they are limited by natural selection.

In 1957 J. B. S. Haldane called attention to the "cost" of natural selection. This occurs whenever allele[1] spreads in a population. Those individuals possessing the allele that is being replaced will be less fit than those possessing the gene that is spreading. A population can only tolerate a limited number of substitutions going on at the same time other-wise too high a proportion of individuals will die, and a viable population cannot be maintained. Haldane's "cost" represents a "substitutional load" in Muller's terminology; Muller's own emphasis should be called a "mutational load". There are other elements to the total load; they all contribute to the idea that there is an upper limit to levels of genetic variation.

In the mid-1960s the application of chemical techniques to a series of proteins studied in a large number of individuals from interbreeding populations showed that very high levels of inherited variation occur in nature: although a few species have a low level of variation, most have a large amount of heterozygosity, i.e. many gene-loci at which different alleles are inherited from the two parents, ranging from 3 or 4 per cent in large animals to around 25 per cent in small ones. Genetic variation is far more common than was previously believed; the theoretical basis of neo-Darwinism, which assumed that

---

[1] allele: a gene carried by an individual; either homozygous (inherited from both parents) or heterozygous (different).

variant genes impose a load on their possessor, seemed to be destroyed.

The simplest way out of the variation dilemma was to assume that the protein variants detected by electrophoresis were selectively neutral: that is, that they had no effect on the breeding success or survival of their carriers. The main positive argument for this conclusion, known as "neutralism", was the apparent accuracy of the "protein clock".

The protein clock is based on the assumption that the substitution of an amino acid at any place in a protein chain is likely to take place at random, and therefore the number of amino acid differences between two species can be regarded as a measure of the time since the species shared a common ancestor. A genealogical tree constructed on this premise would show quantitative degrees of relatedness. When this was done there appeared initially to be remarkable uniformity in rates of substitution in completely different evolutionary lines. However, it soon became clear that different proteins have rates of change differing by nearly a hundredfold. Biochemists speculated about the functional importance of different parts of protein molecules, suggesting that there were "functional constraints" to some parts, whilst other parts were apparently dispensable. This could mean that changes at "unimportant" sites within a molecule might proceed more rapidly than at others, and that other changes might be slowed down. These ideas have been valuable in probing the functional morphology of some well-studied proteins (notably the cytochromes, globins and immunoglobulins), but destroy any idea of an accurate protein clock.

However, the final collapse of the extreme neutralist position came from the recognition that many (and perhaps most) variants change the properties of the proteins in which they are substituted, and are thus potentially subject to selection. This has been shown by studies on biochemical properties *in vitro*, by correlating variant distribution with environmental variables (particularly temperature), and through changes of gene frequencies in time and space. The firm conclusion is that gene frequencies of all sorts are liable to fine adjustment by natural selection.

The theoretical arguments of Muller and Haldane can in retrospect be seen to be rather naïve. Both men effectively thought of every gene acting independently on its carrier. This is patently not true: the entire genetic make-up (or more accurately the phenotype) is selected, not independent aspects of it. Furthermore, selection pressures change in time and space, depending on both the physical and the ecological environment. (This is not Lamarckism: gene transmission is not affected by the environment, although gene expression is.) The genetic composition of a population or species cannot be separated from its history. Indeed, genetic composition is in some ways a record of the impacts and vicissitudes of past environments. Some alleles will respond to current environmental pressures, but others will merely reflect past events. For example, human blood-group frequencies were probably determined by the major epidemic diseases of the past, as individuals died or survived depending on their resistance to particular diseases. Nowadays blood-group differences seem to have little effect on survival.

Judged rather harshly, much of the support for the neutral mutation point of view ("non-Darwinian evolution" as it has been called) came from the elegance of the mathematical arguments rather than their empirical correctness. This does not mean that the neutralist criticisms of neo-Darwinism were completely wrong. Some mutations *will* have no effect on fitness for much of the life of their carriers; the crucial point is that the neutrality of such alleles is unlikely to persist indefinitely.

The neutralist-selectionist controversy had two effects. First it broke the stranglehold of theoreticians on evolutionary biology which had developed during the 1950s and which threatened to turn the subject into a branch of applied mathematics. Secondly, biologists were recalled to biological phenomena in the widest sense (biochemical, immunological, behavioural and physiological, as well as ecological and morphological), and saw the need to resist the temptation to seek all their answers from molecular biology.

The present position

Darwinism has been under attack ever since the *Origin* was published, but the objections raised in the 1860s, 1900s, 1930s and 1960s have all concluded with a strengthening of Darwin's original propositions. A major weakness in Darwin's own understanding of the natural world was resolved with the rediscovery of Mendel's work, and the integration of particulate inheritance into evolutionary theory. This confirmed rather than changed the arguments of the *Origin*. Weismann's theory of germ-line separation and early interpretations of the randomness of mutation were both important in the development of evolutionary thinking and both have had to be modified (the former by the recognition that it only applied to higher animals; the latter by the discovery that much mutation is under biochemical control, and is not simply the result of chance in the statistical sense). Neither affects the neo-Darwinian understanding of biological change.

Despite its survival so far, neo-Darwinism is still being attacked. In the 1980s there is no major objection, but at least five different series of criticisms.

1. *Philosophy*

Uninformed readers are often confused by philosophical discussions about the nature of evolutionary theory. Three assertions are made which need refuting:

a. *Evolution is "only" a theory*. The word "theory" is used in a technical sense by scientists. They distinguish between a set of ideas which are put forward for test, which they call a "hypothesis", and the accumulated synthesis of tested hypotheses, which is a scientific "theory". A theory in this scientific sense is an established interpretation of facts, and is thus quite different from the speculative rationalisations which are called theories in detective novels. A valuable theory combines a host of observations and conclusions into a single whole (and is sometimes called a *paradigm*), and may incorporate some apparent anomalies which are tolerated for the sake of the synthesis (just as physicists accepted Newtonian mechanics although the orbit of Mercury never fitted the predictions); and suggests experiments and tests for further research. The accusation by some authors that evolution is *only* a theory betrays an ignorance of scientific language; when a biologist talks about evolutionary *theory*, he is referring to a corpus of ideas as firmly grounded as any other in his field.

b. *Evolution is survival of the fittest, which is tautologous.* The objection here is to the Darwinian mechanism of evolution, rather than to the fact that evolution has occurred. The argument is that natural selection is the survival of the fittest, but it is the fittest which survive (and reproduce); which is true, but trite. This is another misunderstanding about words: "fitness" in biology is a measure of reproductive success rather than of overall health and vigour, and involves inherited traits which contribute to this success. If these traits are not possessed by all individuals (that is, if variation exists), survival will not be random and will lead to evolutionary change. The claim that natural selection is tautologous amounts merely to a failure to appreciate the factors involved in fitness.

c. *Evolution is non-falsifiable and therefore not a true scientific theory.* The key name associated with this criticism is Karl Popper, who has argued that a scientific theory must be falsifiable, and Darwinian evolution is not falsifiable. There is nothing (it is claimed) which can refute evolutionary theory. For example, the widespread occurrence of organic adaptation is central to Darwinism, but no matter how grotesque or abnormal, a Darwinian can always think up an adaptive evolutionary analysis. However, the fact that speculation has been over-used in evolutionary studies (especially in phylogenetic reconstructions or interpretations of behaviour) does not in itself invalidate the studies.

Indeed, it needs to be emphasised that adaptive or functional explanations are as capable of being experimentally tested as any hypothesis. It is not true that natural selection (or survival of the fittest) is an uncheckable idea. There are many cases where natural selection has been detected (and measured) under natural conditions, and then confirmed by appropriate laboratory experiments: the classical example is Dobzhansky's work on third chromosome inversions in *Drosophila pseudo-obscura*; other examples are the influence of camouflage and warning colouration on survival; of pesticide resistance in rats, mosquitoes, aphids, etc.; of cyanide production and tolerance of heavy metals by plants; of dark pigmentation in ladybirds and land snails living in cloudy areas; and many others. There is no great difficulty in identifying the influence of evolutionary forces acting under describable conditions, although there is a recurring research problem in recognising which characters are affecting fitness themselves, and which are merely markers developmentally or genetically linked to the adaptive trait. This is the explanation of statements by notable biologists such as Simpson that "the fallibility of personal judgment as to the adaptive value of particular characters is notorious;" or Dobzhansky, that "no biologist can judge reliably which 'characters' are neutral, useful, or harmful in a given species". Simpson and Dobzhansky are not in any sense doubting the efficacy of natural selection, but only the prospects of identifying the traits involved in particular adaptive adjustments.

Evolutionary theory is non-scientific in Popper's sense only if certain restrictive definitions about the nature of science are accepted. Philosophers of science argue about the validity and relevance of these definitions. For example, modern evolutionary studies are predictive only in a very limited way. On the other hand, they share similar observational and experimental approaches with other sciences, about which no philosophical doubts are raised. From the point of view of the practising scientists, evolution is as firmly based a science as, say, astronomy or parasitology.

The interpretation of Scripture and the philosophy of science are strange bedfellows, and the only reason for linking them here is that Christian anti-evolutionists frequently cite philosophers to support their particular understanding of the creation narratives. The claim that evolution is not a science is based on a misunderstanding of the concepts and approaches of those who study evolution; to use a secular misunderstanding to back up a disputed interpretation of Scripture is clearly hazardous.

Evolution is a science, but there is much that is called evolution which is not science; it should perhaps be called "evolutionism". It therefore becomes doubly important to understand the real nature of biological evolution in the strict sense.

2. *Punctuated equilibria*

In 1972 two American palaeontologists, Niles Eldredge and Stephen Jay Gould, pointed out that the most marked characteristic of the fossil record was not long-continued change of particular forms, but periods of stability (or stasis), followed by the sudden appearance of a new (albeit related) form. In effect they challenged the prevailing orthodoxy that our lack of knowledge of the origin of fossil species was the result of gaps in the record, and claimed that the unbiased interpretation of fossil successions implies that evolution proceeds by fits and starts. This has been taken by some as an argument for instant (or quantum) speciation, produced by major mutations in the sense of de Vries. In fact Eldredge and Gould proved nothing of the sort: all their emphasis means is that evolutionary rates vary considerably, and that the speciation process is comparatively rapid.

This is not the place to go into the detail of this debate, except to say that suddenness in palaeontological time is different from suddenness in genetical time; the splitting of a lineage can take place very rapidly (in tens rather than thousands of generations) and be produced by a small number of gene differences (as well as by polyploidy, which is the classical method of "instant speciation").

The problem with "punctuated equilibrium" is that critics of Darwinism have equated it with the theory that new species originate from mutations, as postulated by de Vries and Richard Goldschmidt, and so have assumed it is distinct from the speciation process represented by Darwin in the phrase *natura non facit saltum* ("nature does not make a jump"). This assumption is false: Darwin himself was quite clear that evolutionary rates vary. He is explicit in the *Origin of Species* that "the periods during which species have been undergoing modification, though very long as measured by years, have probably been short in comparison with the periods during which these same species remained without undergoing any change", and "I do not suppose that the process (speciation) . . . goes on continuously; it is far more probable that each form remains for long periods unaltered, and then again undergoes modification." G. G. Simpson, in a classical exposition of the neo-Darwinian synthesis [*Tempo and Mode in Evolution*, 1944], stated: "The pattern of steplike evolution that has the appearance of successive structural steps, rather than direct phyletic transitions, is a peculiarity of paleontological data more nearly universal than true rectilinearity." There is no basic conflict between punctuated equilibrium and Darwinian evolution properly understood.

The point that evolutionary rates vary very widely is pertinent to objections that some evolutionary events are so unlikely that they could never have happened by chance. For example, the British astronomer Sir Fred Hoyle has argued that the idea that life originated by random shuffling of molecules is "as ridiculous and improbable as the proposition that a tornado blowing through a junk yard may assemble a Boeing 747". He calculated that the likelihood of life beginning in such a way is one in ten to the power of 40,000 – the chance that 2,000 enzyme molecules will be formed simultaneously from their 20 component amino acids on a single specified occasion. But this is not he correct calculation: the relevant chance is of some far simpler self-replicating system, capable of development by natural selection, being formed at any place on earth, and at any time within a period of 100 million years. We cannot calculate this probability, since we know neither the nature of the hypothetical self-replicating system nor the composition of the "primaeval soup" in which it arose. The origin of life was obviously a rare event, but there is no reason to think that it is as extraordinary or unlikely as Hoyle calculated.

Hoyle's argument is somewhat similar to the often repeated claim that the evolution of complex functioning organs like the human eye or ear by "blind" selection acting on random mutations is as unlikely as a monkey producing the plays of Shakespeare by hitting the keys of a typewriter at random. This completely misunderstands the role and power of natural selection in producing adaptation. R. A. Fisher has commented that "it was Darwin's chief contribution to have brought to light a process by which contingencies a priori improbable are given, in the process of time, an increasing probability, until it is their non-occurrence which becomes highly improbable".

3. Cladism

The classifying of animals and plants (taxonomy) has traditionally been a subjective exercise, controlled by general agreement among specialists as to the reality of particular species. For many years biologists have tried to make classifications more exact. They have used more characters (including chemical and behavioural ones) than the usual morphological criteria, and have increasingly used quantitive multivariate techniques. One particular refinement of this trend is cladism, a method of systematics derived from the work of a German taxonomist, Willi Hennig, and based on a book by him published in English in 1966 (*Phylogenetic Systematics*). Cladism has three axioms:

(i) Features shared by organisms manifest a hierarchical pattern in nature.

(ii) This hierarchical pattern may be economically expressed by means of branching diagrams (cladograms).

(iii) The nodes (branching points) in a cladogram symbolise the homologies (parallels) shared by the organisms linked by the node, so that a cladogram is congruent with a classification.

The cladistic method imposes a discipline on taxonomists, but in the process it has become divorced from evolutionary biology, and especially the working hypothesis of most systematists that they are largely reconstructing phylogeny (evolutionary ancestry) in their classifications. Indeed some cladists explicitly deny that they are concerned with evolution; they claim that they are concerned solely with "pattern" in nature, in ways reminiscent of pre-Darwinian romantics such as Goethe and Geoffroy Saint-Hilaire. In this respect they have departed from Hennig's own method, which was consciously phylogenetic; ironically, the major theoretical contribution of Hennig to classification was in distinguishing between primitive and derived homologies, which is necessary before an evolutionary phylogeny can be constructed.

The cladism controversy has obscured the fundamental principle that while there can be only one true phylogeny for a group (though we may not be sure what it is), classification is more arbitrary, because the rules of classification are made by people for their own convenience. In the words of one of its main protagonists, cladism is "merely rediscovering pre-evolutionary systematics; or if not rediscovering it, fleshing it out". Cladistics is not anti-evolutionary; it is simply irrelevant to a discussion of evolutionary mechanism.

4. Development

The doubts raised by embryologists about Darwinism are the least convincing of the 1980s criticisms. This is not because the problems concerned are trivial or irrelevant, but because of the apparent difficulty of posing them in modern terms. This may be because advances in molecular biology have enabled many of the basic problems in mutation and variation to be set out in very clear-cut terms, but many embryological problems about the origin of pattern and the so-called "laws of form" are still expressed in the almost mystical terms of "morphogenetic fields" used around the turn of the century. Comparatively few biologists have attempted to analyse development genetically (notable exceptions are C. H. Waddington, E. Hadorn, and H. Grüneberg). However molecular biologists have now begun to turn their attention to the effects of gene substitution on organ structure and behaviour. It is clear from the comparatively small amount of work that has been done that gene action early in development may profoundly modify the form and function of the adult, and Waddington (in particular) has shown how genes of small effect can be selected by stresses imposed through the environmental modification of development. There are many links needing to be forged between evolutionary biology and development; it is at best premature to regard embryological criticisms of neo-Darwinism as serious.

5. Neo-Lamarckism

The simplistic idea that characters acquired during life could be inherited by the offspring, as advocated by Jean-Baptiste Lamarck in the early 1800s, had to be abandoned once the physical basis of heredity was worked out. Nevertheless, there have been many attempts to show that some form of Lamarckian inheritance occurs in nature. None had been confirmed.

The most infamous "neo-Lamarckian" episode occurred in Russia between 1948 and 1964. The leader of this movement, T. D. Lysenko, claimed to be able to change the inherited properties of crop plants by grafting or seed treatment, and thereby permanently to improve yield by environmental manipulation. No one outside the USSR was able to repeat these results, and eventually Lysenko was discredited within his own country. Traditional genetics (or "Mendelist-Morganism" as it was called) was suppressed during Lysenko's ascendancy, and many of its practitioners imprisoned. The fact that genes and chromosomes carry heritable material was denied, and replaced by the notion that heredity was a general property of living matter. Lysenko received considerable support from the Soviet authorities because his claims coincided with Marxist ideas of the possibility of socially-driven change. Controversies about the inheritance of intelligence are in some way a continuance of the Lamarckian debate.

Evolutionary biology now

The common characteristic of all the attacks and debates about evolution, past and current, is an over-emphasis on one particular factor or a failure to take into account data from disparate but relevant disciplines. Difficulties in this respect increase as biological knowledge grows, and it becomes difficult to keep different parts of the subject in focus. One reason why the history of evolutionary debate is important is that old arguments tend to recur; indeed one may honestly (if rashly) assert that there is now no real attack on the neo-Darwinian synthesis as it has developed over more than a hundred years.

It is dangerous to suggest that any major set of scientific ideas is close to its final form; as far as neo-Darwinism is concerned, the neutralist debates of the late 1960s and 1970s are still too close to allow complacency (particularly while "creationists" allege that evolutionists have been brainwashed). Nevertheless it seems fair to claim that the neo-Darwinian synthesis is in good shape with new insights gained from the neutralist debates on the maintenance of variation and the interaction of genes with ecology; and that there is no need for any major new synthesis to incorporate the attacks of the 1980s.

6

"Creationism" and science

Much dreaming and many words are meaningless.
Therefore stand in awe of God.

Ecclesiastes 5:7

The question "Evolution or Creation?" is misleading, because it implies that one or the other is false. In fact, both are true: the evidence for evolution comes from science; the evidence for creation comes from faith [Hebrews 11:3]. Yet evolution and creation are commonly treated as incompatible opposites. The reason for this is neither scriptural nor scientific, as the last three chapters have shown; this chapter examines some of the arguments of present-day "creationists" to test if the complementarity of evolution and creation which emerges from a straightforward account of Biblical exegesis and evolutionary biology needs modifying in any way. As we do this, it is worth recalling an important insight of William Temple, who pointed out that Jesus himself "so often does not answer enquirers' questions, but leads to ground where the question does not arise at all" [*Readings in John's Gospel*, 1939]. Many of the questions in the evolution and Christianity debate only arise because they wrongly assume some basic premise; time and time again it is worth probing behind the question to find if it is worth asking, or whether it should be re-phrased.

The first thing to note is that the pre-Darwinian understanding of the world (based, as we have seen, on Greek, especially Plato's, philosophy) is incompatible with a situation where species and environments are in ever-changing interactions. Only when the inadequacy of the old assumptions was recognised could evolutionary possibilities even be considered. And there was no reason to challenge the classical framework until it became obviously faulty. One of the most influential books of the nineteenth century was William Paley's *Natural Theology: Or, Evidences of the Existence and Attributes of the Deity Collected from the Appearance of Nature* [1802] which was a forceful exposition of God as the Great Watchmaker (it impressed Darwin considerably when he read it as an undergraduate at Cambridge). Paley argued that each part of an animal's body is useful to it in its way of life, and that this universal adaptation illustrates the wisdom and benevolence of a God who cares for His creatures. Just as the intricate structure of a watch implies a watchmaker so the incredible complexity of living things proclaims the power of their Designer. This was followed by the eight Bridgewater Treatises (so-called because they were commissioned in the will of the Eighth Earl of Bridgewater) in which the authors used various scientific subjects to demonstrate "the Power, Wisdom, and Goodness of God as manifested in the Creation". Perhaps the final major defence of the old understanding was Philip Gosse's *Omphalos: an Attempt to Untie the Geological Knot* [1857]. Gosse was a distinguished naturalist. He was also a member of the Plymouth Brethren. His book was a discussion as to whether Adam had had a navel (*omphalos*) or not. Since he regarded Adam to be a special creation and not the son of a natural mother, Gosse argued there was no anatomical reason why he should have had one. However, he would not then have been like all his descendants, so Gosse concluded that God created him with a navel. Using a similar argument, Gosse maintained that the Garden of Eden into which God placed Adam would have had trees created in the same week as Adam, but they would be "as if" they had lived many years. Likewise, God created the rocks with fossils already in them (possibly to confuse "godless scientists"). To the present-day reader, Gosse's ratiocinations seem gloriously implausible (although "creationists" who believe in a strict six day creation still hold to a very similar "apparent age" theory), but his logic is impeccable. There is no way of directly testing his arguments.

In the 1980s we are in a very different situation. Now that the only people who seriously deny that evolution has occurred are "creationists", the debates in the scientific community are all concerned with particular parts of the *mechanism* of evolution. The distinguished American geneticist R. C. Lewontin has exhorted biologists to emphasise this:

> It is time for students of the evolutionary process, especially those who have been misquoted and used by the creationists, to state clearly that evolution is *fact*, not theory, and that what is at issue within biology are questions of details of the process and the relative importance of different mechanisms of evolution. It is a *fact* that the earth, with liquid water, is more than 3.6 billion years old. It is a *fact* that cellular life has been around for at least half of that period and that organised multicellular life is at least 800 million years old. It is a *fact* that major life forms now on earth were not all represented in the past. There were no birds or mammals 250 million years ago. It is a *fact* that major forms of the past are no longer living. There used to be dinosaurs and *Pithecanthropus*, and there are none now. It is a *fact* that all living forms come from previous living forms. Therefore, all present forms of life arose from ancestral forms which were different. Birds arose from nonbirds and humans from nonhumans. No person who pretends to any understanding of the natural world can deny these facts any more than she or he can deny that the earth is round, rotates on its axis, and revolves round the sun.

How do the "creationists" maintain their belief that evolution has not occurred? Several American books have been published which answer "creationism" in detail (see

"Further Reading", p. 173), and the following is merely a summary of the key points. The most substantial "creationist" books are *The Genesis Flood* by J. C. Whitcomb and H. M. Morris [published in 1961], and *Scientific Creationism* [1974a], edited by H. M. Morris (which is published in two editions, a General Edition, and a Public School Edition which omits a chapter on "Creation according to Scripture"). There are many other "creationist" volumes, but they are almost entirely derivative from these two. The most important British books are *The Great Brain Robbery* [1975] by D. C. C. Watson and *Bone of Contention* [1976] by Sylvia Baker.

Interpretation

Fossils

"Creationists" use two arguments: that fossil stratigraphy is based on a circular argument; and that the Great Deluge (Noah's Flood) disrupted fossiliferous strata so much that the main evidence for evolution – the fossil record – is useless for the purpose. The fossil evidence that life has evolved from simple to complex forms over the geological ages depends on the geological ages of the specific rocks in which these fossils are found; that the rocks, however, are assigned geological ages based on the fossil assemblages which they contain; that the fossils, in turn, are arranged on the basis of their assumed evolutionary relationships. Thus the main evidence for evolution is based on the assumption of evolution [see Morris, 1977].

However, this is wrong. Biostratigraphy starts from key fossil species in horizontally layered fossil bearing rocks. Because the sequence of the fossil succession is always the same wherever it occurs, geologists are able to infer that rocks with the same fossils are the same age. This can be checked by tracing fossil-bearing beds laterally where this is possible. The irony is that biostratigraphy was developed by men who were all "creationists" (p. 29). The father of stratigraphy, William Smith, noted in 1817, "My observations on this and other branches of the subject are entirely original and unencumbered with theories, for I have none to support."

Radiometric and other dating techniques

Absolute dating of rock strata has become possible with the development of methods for determining the relative proportions of radioactive isotopes. Knowing the rate at which these break down, it is possible to extrapolate back to the time when the rock (or fossil, or other artefact) was laid down. There are three methods in common use (rubidium-strontium, potassium-argon, uranium-lead). "Creationists" argue that they are intrinsically unreliable because the system being dated must be "closed" (*i.e.* unaffected by extraneous factors); must have originally contained no daughter products; and the radioactive decay rate must always have been the same. In fact the first criterion is only relevant with reference to contamination by breakdown products; the second is not correct because there are other methods of estimating the amount originally present; and the third introduces a much more general point about the uniformity of nature. While it is possible that there are factors that may influence the decay rates of radioactive elements, nothing is yet known of them (increased pressure and temperature certainly have no effect). "Creationists" have suggested that cosmic rays should speed up decay rates, but even if this were true it would not affect radiometric dating, because cosmic rays do not penetrate far into the ground. Experiments by Robert Gentry and his colleagues cited by "creationists" (e.g. Slusher, 1981), suggesting that variation in the "halo" of radioactivity around a decaying radioactive nucleus indicates variation in decay rates have not been confirmed by other workers, and later had to be retracted in part [see Dalrymple, 1982; Brush, 1982]. Available evidence indicates that radioactive decay rates are indeed constant, and have been so throughout earth history.

In practice, crucial dates are always repeated by more

than one technique. Radiometric dating has now been in use for long enough to conclude that the degree of consistency both between the results obtained by different methods applied to the same material and between radiometric dates and a geological time-scale based on criteria of another sort are too high to be dismissed.

In *The Scientific Case for Evolution* [1977], Morris listed seventy estimates of the age of the earth, ranging from 100 years to 500 million years. He pointed out that all were based on the "uniformitarian" assumption that a process has gone on at the same rate in the past as now. Hence, he concluded, not one of the estimates is reliable. However, a number of the processes he refers to are based on the flowing of various elements into the ocean, the cooling of the earth, and the erosion of sediments; he does not record that scientists now have definite reasons to suppose that such rates did vary in the past (and also have definite reasons for supposing that radioactive decay did not vary). For example, as long ago as 1936 Arthur Holmes gave a detailed explanation why the salinity of the oceans could not give accurate estimates of the earth's age, but some "creationists" still use these estimates in their attempt to shake the credibility of standard dating techniques.

Thomas Barnes (Dean of the Graduate School of the Institute of Creation Research) has argued that decay in the earth's magnetic field must imply its recent creation. His starting assumption was that the field owed its existence to electric currents that are not maintained by a dynamo or any other energy source but are decaying exponentially with time as their energy is dissipated into heat. This assumption is flatly contradicted by almost all current research on geomagnetism and is not even supported by the observational data that Barnes himself presented.

Barnes determined the parameters of his exponential decay curve from measurements of the earth's magnetic dipole in 1835 and 1965 (ignoring the fact that the decay is very nearly linear, *not* exponential, between those dates) and then extrapolated the curve backwards to 20,000 BC Since the field would thus have the incredibly large value of eighteen thousand gauss, he concluded that the earth must have been created after that time.

But recent research in archaeomagnetism shows that the extrapolation is invalid. To justify his calculation, Barnes had to reject the Elsasser theory (now generally accepted, at least qualitatively, by geophysicists) that the earth's magnetic field is maintained by the dynamo action of fluid motions in the core. He also had to reject the conclusion (an integral part of the modern theory of plate tectonics or continental drift) that the earth's magnetic field has completely reversed itself several times in the past. J. A. Jacobs, the one independent authority on whom Barnes relies, has recently decided that this conclusion is now firmly established, thus undermining the basis of Barnes's calculation.

At the present time the evidence is overwhelming that the earth is several billion years old; many different determinations by radioactive dating methods give an age close to 4.5 billion years. The criticisms of radioactive dating published by "creationists" have no accepted scientific basis and can be justified only by arbitrarily rejecting well-established results of modern physical science. Their argument from the decay of the earth's magnetic field for a young (10,000-year-old) earth is completely refuted by empirical data and is incompatible with all currently accepted principles of geomagnetism [Brush, 1982].

Entropy

A common "creationist" argument is that evolution is impossible because it runs counter to the Second Law of Thermodynamics, which involves the concept of entropy. This is, crudely speaking, that disorder inevitably increases in any system with the passage of time. This means that the increase in diversity and complexity which, in general, accompanied evolution cannot possibly take place. The fallacy in this conclusion is that entropy only increases in a "closed" system, one that does not receive any energy from outside. Now the earth continually receives vast amounts of energy from the sun, which is sufficient to more than counteract any downhill tendencies in the living world. The "creationist" response to this is that closed systems do not in fact exist; all systems are open, and "It is obvious that the Laws of Thermodynamics apply to open systems as well since they have only been tested and proved on open systems" [Morris, *The Troubled Waters of Evolution*, 1974b:125]. Although this reply is true, it is misleading, because it ignores the amount of energy exchange between system and surroundings; living organisms (which are the subject of evolution) receive and lose such large amounts of energy that there is no way that they can be "as if" it were closed.

Another "creationist" approach to entropy uses analogy: "Why don't battered Volkswagens in junkyards order themselves into shiny new Cadillacs? A junkyard is an open system" [Wysong, *The Creation-Evolution Controversy*, 1976:244]. The short answer to this is that change in ageing motor cars is utterly different to change in a living organism. But the real point is that open-system thermodynamics is *not sufficient* for the decreased entropy (i.e. increased order) of life; it merely shows that decreased entropy is possible in an open system. In fact the true parallel between evolution and a scrap-yard would be the recycling of the decrepit cars (involving the input of new energy), in which the battered run-down materials do in fact achieve new life in "shiny new Cadillacs".

Species and kinds

"Creationists" accept conventional mechanisms for genetical change, and agree that some changes have happened. They have no problems, for example, with the spread of melanic forms in many moth species in the early years of the industrial revolution, which restored the camouflage of the moths as they rested on tree trunks which had become covered with a black deposit from smoke. The sticking point is change between "kinds" because God made "plant bearing seeds according to their kinds and trees bearing fruit with seed in it according to their kinds . . . the wild animals according to their kinds, the livestock according to their kinds, and all the creatures that move along the ground according to their kinds"; what is denied is that evolutionary modification ever transgresses the boundary between "basic kinds".

What is a "kind"? There are differences among "creationists". Hiebert [*Evolution. Its Collapse in View?*, 1979:37] asserts that basic kinds correspond "roughly to the arbitrary category of species"; Morris [*Scientific Creationism*, 1974a: 180] uses intersterility for assigning organisms to different kinds, although Wysong [*The Evolution–Creation Controversy*, 1976:59] distinguishes species from kinds, on the grounds that the former are defined by intersterility; Gish [*Evolution. The Fossils Say No!* 1978:32] is more specific (albeit tautologous), "a basic animal or plant kind includes all animals or plants which were truly derived from a single stock"; Lester & Bohlin [1984:162] use the same definition, "all organisms that are descended from a single created population"; finally Arthur Jones [*The Genetic Integrity of Kinds*, 1981] has suggested that a "kind" depends on the structure of its cell membrane rather than its normal genes.

It is easy to see why "creationists" leave matters vague. As Gish candidly remarks, basic kinds are those that descend from an original stock. This will not do as a definition, of course, since the point of dispute concerns which organisms descend from the same original stock. Yet Gish's comment serves to remind us that the point of the enterprise is to identify the boundaries across which evolution is not to occur. What are the possibilities?

One possible line is suggested by Hiebert: basic kinds are species. But this will lead to trouble because evolutionary theorists can produce clear and well-understood examples of trans-specific evolution. Darwin's finches on the Galapagos Islands are different species, and the genus *Drosophila* includes numerous species with well-charted relationships.

Now it would clearly be counterproductive to identify basic kinds with some standard taxonomic category above the species level; to propose, for example, that basic kinds are genera or families. The problem is that "creationists" want to claim that some species, like *Homo sapiens*, are basic kinds. What is needed is a concept of kind that cuts across the standard taxonomic hierarchy. The main suggestion offered is that organisms belonging to the same kind are interfertile. In fact, this does not help.

Notwithstanding that appeal to the interfertility criterion does mark as distinct kinds species that in fact have a clear evolutionary relationship. There are species of *Drosophila*, for example, whose chromosomes are clearly derived from a common ancestor, but that divide up the chromosomal material differently. Most of these species are unable to produce fertile hybrids. Some are unable to produce any hybrids at all. But there is a problem from the other direction. Appeal to interfertility allows lions and tigers to belong to the same kind. If this usage of *kind* is strictly observed, are we to assume that some common ancestor of lions and tigers was originally created, and that lions and tigers have since evolved from that common ancestor? Or did the Creator originally make several "varieties" of some kinds? For example, in creating some feline kind, were lions and tigers made separately as "individual varieties"? If so, what was the rationale for favouring some kinds with different "varieties"? If not, the "creationist" must assume some very rapid events of diversification (the emergence of lions and tigers from a common feline ancestor; of dogs, wolves, and jackals from a common canine ancestor).

Yet it is not clear that a retreat into vagueness helps. For example, Gish believes that "the gibbons, orangutans, chimpanzees, and gorillas would each be included in a different basic kind" [Gish, 1979: 37]. This decision deprives him of any ability to borrow evolutionary explanations of the many great similarities among these primates. From the molecular biologists' discoveries of close kinship in molecular structures of proteins to the well-established similarities of anatomical structure, there is a host of details that cry out for explanation in terms of common ancestry. "Creationists" recognise the power of using common ancestry to explain the chromosomal similarities among species of fruit flies or the kinship of the Galapagos finches but draw the line at using the same type of explanation to account for other powerful similarities (such as the kinship of the gibbons and the great apes). Yet, having applied the pattern of evolutionary explanation where it suits their purposes to do so, "creationists" refrain from applying it elsewhere – and this is the crux – they offer no *coherent account of the distinction between the cases.* They offer us a hotch-potch, picking and choosing from evolutionary theory, not by applying some principled criterion but by tailoring the concept of kind to suit the needs of the moment.

One final point: Gish's list of basic kinds identifies bats, an entire diverse order, containing more than 850 species, as a single kind. (The variation among bats is enormous; there is a wide range of dietary habits, sizes and flight pattern; some bats see, others do not.) Yet in the primate order, the family *Pongidae* (great apes and gibbons) is divided into four separate kinds. Why? The morphological similarities among the pongids are extensive, but to admit these as important evidence of common ancestry would be to flirt with disaster. Humans are just not that different from the great apes. Differences that are dismissed in the cases of bats and cats (and, no doubt, bees and trees, whales and snails) suddenly become important when a major tenet of "creationism" might be threatened.

Evolutionary Biology

Turning from "creationism" to evolutionary biology, there is dispute whether there are differences between *microevolution* (i.e. evolutionary changes up to the species level) and *macroevolution.* Macroevolution is impossible if new species are not formed, because by definition all members of an existing species are capable of interbreeding and thus pooling their characteristics. However a species may be divided (by time, physical or ecological barriers, and/or reproductively isolation), and then the only constraints on divergence are those of the availability of variation and organisation of the genetic material. Put another way, any evolutionary adjustment must be based on a single pool of genes (that is, a species); divergence and diversity can only arise when that pool becomes two or more (that is, following speciation). Greenwood [1979] has expressed this formally:

> The term macroevolution is generally used to account for the origin of "higher" categories, yet these higher categories are in effect only our attempts to reflect simultaneously both the increasing diversity and the relationships of organisms within an evolving phyletic lineage. A lineage must stem from a single species. Its further development and diversification will depend on speciation events. I would equate macroevolution with speciation . . .

In other words, as soon as separate species arise (*i.e.* groups unable to cross-breed successfully), there is the possibility of both long-term and large-scale changes. The key issue is, therefore, whether new species can ever come into being.

It is impossible to know exactly what happened in past evolutionary events – as, for example, when the arthropods separated from the annelids or the flowering plants from the gymnosperms. However, there is no problem about accepting the possibility of these changes, *if* there has been sufficient time for them, and *if* new species may be formed from existing ones.

It has often been said that the one topic that Darwin did not deal with in the *Origin of Species* was the origin of species. There has been a tendency to assume that this means that, even now, nothing is known about the process. This is not true. Addition of chromosome sets (polyploidy) producing sterility when crossed with the parent stock has been known for a long time to be a major factor in plant speciation. However, our knowledge of molecular mechanisms in biology (especially the way in which genes function and the role of gene duplication), and of the factors controlling variation in natural populations has only recently reached the stage where experimental study of the speciation process can sensibly take place. Speciation actually in progress has now been investigated in many cases, notable examples being that of Hawaiian *Diptera*, snails in the Society Islands, and Lake Victoria cichlid fishes. Moreover, improved techniques of studying chromosomes have permitted new insights into cytological differentiation and its correlation with changes in the genes themselves.

Our current knowledge of speciation is an excellent example of how science advances. We have already noted that missing links are relatively rare in fossil series. In fact a common feature in fossil-bearing strata is the persistence of a particular form for a long period without change, followed by its apparently abrupt replacement by a similar but distinct form, i.e. the sudden appearance of a new species. (This sequence, incidentally, is difficult to explain on a simple "creationist" model, even if extinction is allowed.) Hawaiian *Drosophila* exhibit today, in a living fauna, exactly the same characteristics of lack of variability and rapid formation of new species that palaeontologists recognise in fossils; *and* it has been possible to reconstruct the speciation process, and repeat it in the laboratory.

These advances in our understanding of the nature of speciation do not mean that our previous lack of knowledge of the process was wrong in any moral sense, but merely that earlier ideas have been clarified or modified as information grows. This is how science develops. But it must be emphasised that the overall effect of our better understanding of what goes on in nature has been to confirm the reality of the species as a discrete breeding unit and its role as the crucial element underlying (macro) evolutionary change. The modern biologist differs little in this from the biologists of the Victorian age; the main difference is that we now know the mechanisms by which species can be formed.

The extent of evolution

Microevolution is a fact; macroevolution is not, in the same sense. Darwin commented in the *Origin of Species* that the belief that all forms of life are descended from few or even one ancestor is argument by analogy, and "analogy may be a deceitful guide". New species certainly arise. Because of the virtual uniformity of the genetic code in all living things, evolutionists in general tend to assume that all forms of life are descended from a single origin – or, at most, two or three origins. Christian evolutionists have been divided on this point; some at least believe that a number of independent acts of special creation may have taken place, establishing the main groups of animals and plants. Rendle-Short, for example, took this attitude in his influential *Modern Discovery and the Bible*. Some modern "creationists" also come close to this view, interpreting the word translated "kinds" (of animals and plants) as indicating major groups rather than species. However, there is no real evidence for this position. Unless there is clear biblical indication to the contrary, there is no particular reason to deny that most and possibly all forms of life have a common ancestor – and in Scripture we have the suggestion from the use of *bara* that God created biological life once only.

Other criticisms of evolutionary ideas that occur in "creationist" literature have been referred to in previous chapters, in particular the notion that "perfect" adaptations (like the vertebrate eye or ear) could not result from a "blind sieve" like natural selection (p. 41), that mutations are always deleterious (p. 87), that miracles (including creation) can have no natural explanation and are always instanteous (p. 52), and that no missing link has ever been found (p. 117). It is worth making three points:

1. *Missing links do occur*

This is a matter of fact, and reference to palaeontological literature will show that more are continually being discovered. However, an article by Cuffey [1972] is worth quoting, because it was published in an evangelical journal as a specific contribution "toward resolving the evolution controversy". Cuffey lists (with references) several hundred transitional forms, including many "crossing from one higher taxon into another". He concluded:

> The palaeontologic record displays numerous sequences of transitional fossils, oriented appropriately within the independently derivable geo-chronologic time framework, and morphologically and chronologically connecting earlier species with later species (often so different that the end-members are classified in different high-rank taxa). These sequences quite overwhelmingly support an evolutionary, rather than a *fiat*-creationist, view of the history of life. Consequently, after carefully considering the implication of the fossil record, we must conclude that the record represents the remains of gradually and continually evolving, ancestor-descendent lineages, uninterrupted by special creative acts, and producing successive different species which eventually become so divergent from the initial form that they constitute new major kinds of organisms.

In contrast, Gish has written in *Evolution: The Fossils Say No!*:

> While transitions at the subspecies level are observable and some at the species level may be inferred, the absence of transitional forms between higher categories (the created kinds of the creation model) is regular and systematic.

Sylvia Baker stated bluntly in *Bone of Contention*: "Apart from archaeopteryx (a primitive bird), nothing in the fossil record suggests a convincing link between animals of different types."

These statements are wrong.[1]

2. *An evolutionist would expect missing links to be rare.*

Notwithstanding the well-documented occurrence of many transitional forms, there is no denying the fact that they are rare. One reason for this is that they must have been present in far fewer numbers than both their ancestral and descendent forms. Another is that evolution proceeds at very different rates in different groups at different times. The key macroevolutionary event is speciation (see above), and it is now clear that this can be an extremely rapid process followed by a "genetic revolution" when change can be very marked. In some ways, it is surprising that there are so many missing links known.

3. *Function* does *change with structure*

Sir Andrew Huxley (grandson of Thomas Henry Huxley, and a Nobel laureate) takes up a point made specifically by Bishop Wilberforce in his British Association debate with T. H. Huxley (Huxley, 1982):

> Wilberforce quotes Owen (Director of the Natural History Museum in London, and determined opponent of Darwin) on the apparent origin of mammals in Mesozoic times. The hallmark of a mammal may be said to lie in its

---

[1] Sir Fred Hoyle and some associates have claimed that the *Archaeopteryx* fossils are forgeries, with feathers etched on to a dinosaur skeleton. This accusation has been comprehensively answered by senior scientists at the British Museum (Natural History) [Charig *et al.*, 1986]. The arguments are too technical to be summarised here; essentially they indicate that Hoyle *et al* were unfamiliar with the appearance of fossils in general, and interpreted appearances of the *Archaeopteryx* BM(NH) fossil as signs of human interference. Charig *et al* [1986] make the point that five other specimens of this "missing link" are known, discovered at different times between 1855 and 1956, and it is impossible to conceive that a forger interfered with them all. Moreover, the BM(NH) specimen was acquired and described by Darwin's arch-antagonist, Richard Owen, and it is difficult to believe that he would have produced evidence that supported Darwin and made a fool of Owen himself if the original forgery had been his responsibility (which Hoyle *et al* suggest).

lower jaw, consisting as it does of a single bone (the "dentary") which articulates directly with the skull, while the lower jaw of a reptile is only partly formed of the dentary, which articulates with the skull through four other bones. The differences enables us mammals to chew, while reptiles as a rule swallow their prey whole. Further, in every mammal two of the small bones (ossicles) in the middle ear are derived from embryonic structures which in a reptile give rise to two of these bones which form the joint between jaw and skull. Until 1958 there was no evidence of a series of intermediate forms which could both eat and hear. But in 1958 two independent descriptions of "missing links" possessing *both* types of joint, on a common exis across the skull, were published [*Diathrognathus; Morganucodon*]. In the later Mesozoic mammals, the reptilian type of joint has disappeared, leaving only the mammalian type and freeing the quadrate and articular for conversion into incus and malleus respectively. However, intermediate stages in this conversion have not yet been found as fossils (perhaps because the bones are so small and delicate), and it has not been clear that the conversion would have been favoured by natural selection since the advantages claimed in current textbooks for the mammalian system of ossicles over the reptilian columella are not convincing. (The lever action of incus and malleus contributes something toward matching the fluid in the inner ear to the air, but this matching is done mostly by the ratio of areas between eardrum and footplate of columella or stapes which acts as a piston on the inner ear fluid, and is easily adjusted by altering the area of this piston.)

The irony of this situation is that a unique and important function for the ossicular chain was put forward and, as far as I can see, was conclusively established by beautiful experiments nearly half a century ago by Ernst Bárány who showed that the effective centre of mass of the ossicular chain is close to the axis by which incus and malleus are pivoted to the skull, so that when the skull undergoes vibratory movements the ossicles move with the skull and there is no relative motion by which the inner ear can be excited. Internal noises due to chewing, breathing and so forth are thus reduced by several orders of magnitude, with a corresponding improvement in signal:noise ratio for the detection of external sounds. I have no doubt whatever that this is the advantage for which the steps leading to the mammalian middle ear were selected; further, it is easy to imagine smaller improvements in the same direction being given by much cruder arrangements before the mammalian system of ossicles was perfected.

Huxley goes on to describe a physiological discovery which has made acceptable a difficulty raised by Darwin in the *Origin* whilst discussing "Organs of extreme perfection and complication". Concerning the electric organs of fish, Huxley points out that the Darwinian:

Has to demonstrate if he can, not only the existence of intermediate forms but their usefulness to their possessors in the struggle for existence. As Darwin says of these organs "in the Gynmotus and Torpedo they no doubt serve as powerful means of defence and perhaps for securing prey"; he mentions the existence in other fishes of much weaker electric organs which can indeed be regarded as intermediate between ordinary muscles and the powerful electric organs, but he was unable to suggest a way in which these weaker organs might be useful. This gap was filled thirty years ago by Hans Lissmann, who showed that the possessors of these organs have a sixth sense which we lack, in that they are sensitive to extraordinarily small changes in the electric field in the water in which they are swimming. Pulses from the weak electric organs are detected by this sensory system and distortions of the field indicate the presence of obstacles with a lower conductivity than the water or – in freshwater fishes – of animal prey with a higher conductivity.

I will forbear from discussing Noah's Ark in detail because it is too easy to stray from literalism into parody or sarcasm. According to Gish [1979] there would have been room in the Ark (accepting its dimensions as given in Genesis 6:15f) for the equivalent of 80,000 sheep. As there are at present (according to Gish) about 20,000 air-breathing, land-running species of animals on earth and another 20,000 species are now extinct, Noah would have had to load 40,000 pairs of animals. However, this does not take into account the smaller inhabitants, including many parasites and communicable diseases, for which the human race is the only host. Noah and his family would have had to carry tapeworms, malaria, parasites, hookworm, pinworm, lice and so on. The non-human animals would have similar burdens. Gish [loc. cit] suggests that the dinosaurs in the Ark were babies, so that there would have been room for them. He also believes that "God caused these creatures to hibernate and lowered their rate of metabolism to such a low level that they required very little food and produced very little waste". This does not solve the diet of the animals when they left the Ark; for obvious reasons the carnivores could not eat the herbivores, when there was only a single pair of each species.

These comments are not meant to detract from a proper interpretation of the Ark and the Flood, but only to draw attention to the distortions forced by extreme literalism. The crux of the story is that righteousness comes by faith [Hebrew 11:7]; it is not intended to convey a message about animal husbandry.

The "creationist" case

A frequent complaint of "creationists" is that Darwinian biology is unfalsifiable. We have already considered the formal philosophical status of evolutionary theory (pp. 94–7), but it is worth repeating that evolution is to biology what the Periodic Table is to chemistry. Sir Peter Medawar has written:

It is naïve to suppose that the acceptance to evolutionary theory depends on the evidence of a number of so-called "proofs"; it depends rather upon the fact that the evolutionary theory permeates and supports every branch of biological science, much as the notion of the roundness of the earth underlies all geodesy and all cosmological theories on which the shape of the earth has a bearing. Thus anti-evolutionism is of the same stature as flat-earthism.

This is not to claim that specific evolutionary ideas are not open to test. The importance of punctuated equilibrium and the distinction between micro- and macroevolution are two areas of current research in evolutionary biology. Similarly, if "creationists" were able to produce any facts or interpretations which challenge accepted evolutionary concepts, they would have to be taken seriously. However, most "creationist science" is little more than partially informed polemic. But one "fact" needs consideration.

The Paluxy river bed in central Texas contains:

> Large numbers of both dinosaur and human footprints. The tracks occur in trails, and in two or three locations, the dinosaur and human trails cross each other, with two known cases where human and dinosaur tracks actually overlap each other. This particular case cannot be dismissed as an example of "re-working" of two original distinct fossil deposits . . . It seems that the only possible escape from the conclusion that man and dinosaurs were contemporary is to say that the human tracks were not really human but were made by some unknown two-legged animal with feet like human feet! [Morris, *Scientific Creationism*, p. 122].

"Creationists" have placed considerable emphasis on the Paluxy findings, but there have always been difficulties with them. Many of the tracks are not readily distinguished, even by expert palaeontologists; for example, one print was measured as 381 mm long by one "creationist" and 229 mm by another; measurements of the size of the prints in the same track show differences, even when made by the same person; in some cases, there are disagreements whether a particular footprint is left or right. Furthermore, individual prints have essentially an even depth at all points, whereas real human footprints are very poorly defined in the instep, in comparison to the heel and toe, where the walking process produces indentations. Worse, some local inhabitants in the Paluxy region used to make money by carving tracks in pieces of rock. There is photographic evidence that some tracks have deepened between successive photographs. Finally, many of the man-tracks in the soft limestone have now weathered to such a degree that what were previously identified as human footprints are now apparently clear three-toed dinosaur tracks. William Tanner, a senior American geologist and Christian, describes the situation thus: "It seems clear that we are dealing with carvings made by human beings, not by human feet. They are probably a couple of centuries old, but I do not believe that they are as much as 1,000 years old. However in no case are they as old as the rock, no matter what the actual age of the rock might be. Perhaps they are American Indian ceremonial carvings." John Morris the "creationist" author of a book on the Paluxy footprints [*Tracking Those Incredible Dinosaurs and the People Who Knew Them*, 1980] and son of Henry Morris, has now conceded that there is no scientifically acceptable evidence of human footprints in the Paluxy limestones, and a film based on them has been withdrawn [Thulborn, 1986].

Tanner [1981] has written:

The rock record, despite diligent search by many determined to find positive evidence of a brief earth history, has not revealed any such evidence. All of the evidence cited by them has been based on simple misreading of elementary facts. The so-called Precambrian human footprints of North Carolina (which I have examined and are neither Precambrian nor footprints), the supposed

Cretaceous human fetus of Oklahoma (which is neither human nor a fetus), the reported Noachian deluge deposits of various places (which were neither simultaneous nor catastrophic): all of these are citations by persons who are willing to mis-state the observable and the verifiable facts of geology in order to support what they consider to be a biblical doctrine . . . Geology *requires* a very long history and the Bible *permits* a very long history . . . The simplest best statement of fact concerning the creation controversy is: we do not yet know the final word, but the evidence points strongly in the direction of a torturously slow development, as God's purposes have been carried out according to the schedule of His choosing.

The honest truth is that wherever one reviews the anti-evolutionary evidence produced by "creationists" or examines their criticisms of orthodox evolutionary theory, one finds gaps or errors. The "creationist" case does not stand up. Even worse, it is easy to find examples where arguments have been used dishonestly or annotations distorted. The discredited fraud of Piltdown man is frequently cited as an example of the duplicity of evolutionists, although orthodox palaeontologists always had difficulty with it, and were relieved when it was exposed as a fake. The continued quoting of Piltdown needs to be set against "creationist" ploys, such as Bowden [in *Ape-man: Fact and Fallacy*, 1977:84] quoting a distinguished palaeontologist who had described *Sinanthropus pekinensis* on the basis of a single tooth and "was naturally concerned to legitimise this creation when he had to describe a skull cap", when all the palaeontologist was concerned with was a doubt whether the new genus was really any different from the previously described *Pithecathropus* [q.v. see Groves, 1986]. I do not mean to infer any deliberate dishonesty here, but to point out that nuances like this make one's case stronger to someone who does not know the full background.

Along the sames lines, "creationists" frequently quote a

statement of Lord Zuckerman: "if man evolved from an apelike creature, he did so without leaving a trace of that evolution in the fossil record", whereas the full quotation is: "No scientists could logically dispute the proposition that man, without having been involved in any act of creation, evolved from some apelike creature in a very short space of time – speaking in geological terms – without leaving any fossil traces of the steps of the transformation" [Zuckerman, 1970:64].

I have no wish or evidence to impugn the integrity of "creationists", but they are enthusiasts and skilled in debating, whereas most scientists are not interested in or practised in debate. For example, "creationist" writings spend much space on discussions about the inadequacies of morphological characteristics, vestigial organs and the like, whereas one of the problems about morphological traits is that they can have arisen in more than one way; they do not offer firm support either to evolutionists or to anti-evolutionists. As a matter of history, morphological data played very little part in the neo-Darwinian synthesis of the 1930s. Clearly, if evolution has taken place, there are likely to be signs of relationship between living forms. However biochemical data are much more convincing than morphological (for example, DNA code, amino acid sequences of proteins, hormone structure and function, biochemical polymorphisms, chromosome structure, etc.); detailed comparisons between man and the other apes have been carried out for such characteristics. Again, one of the most convincing reasons for accepting evolution in the nineteenth century was the explanation it provided for the facts of the uneven geographical distribution of animals and plants, with different forms characteristic of particular geographical regions, and many peculiar species found only on oceanic islands. Yet "creationists" rarely discuss biogeography. In their seminal book, *The Genesis Flood* [1961], Whitcomb and Morris wrote:

The more we study the fascinating story of animal distribution around the earth, the more convinced we have become that this vast river of variegated life forms, moving ever outward from the Asiatic mainland, across the continents and seas, has not been a chance and haphazard phenomenon. Instead, *we see the hand of God guiding and directing these creatures in ways that man, with all his ingenuity, has never been able to fathom*, in order that the great commission to the postdiluvian animal kingdom might be carried out, and "that they may breed abundantly in the earth, and be fruitful, and multiply upon the earth" (Genesis. 8:17). [p. 86]

Morris has subsequently written very little about biogeography; the subject is just not discussed.

The difficulties about debate with "creationists" are illustrated by the experience of W. Z. Pollitzer [1980], who devoted a Presidential Address to the American Association of Physical Anthropologists to an account of a meeting he shared with the head of the Creation Research Institute:

I outlined briefly the classic evidence for evolution, for I believe we need to present this anew to every generation of students: the arguments from comparative anatomy, the remarkable parallels in embryology, that striking geographical distribution of organisms that so impressed Darwin on the voyage of the Beagle, the ever-increasing data from palaeontology including so many recent primate fossil finds, and the observation of cultivated plants and domesticated animals. To these I added the newer knowledge from karyotypes (chromosomes), immunology, and biochemistry. And I concluded with an outline of such mechanisms of evolution as mutation, selection, and those isolating factors that turn populations into species; in a variety of organisms from pine trees and fruit flies to birds and frogs, we can today witness the evolutionary process.

I cannot claim that I understood the argument of my opponent. It appeared to consist largely of quotations out of context from alleged authorities that, somehow, were said to indicate that evolution could not occur. He claimed that evolution would contradict the second law of thermodynamics, although that law only holds in a closed system and not on our earth constantly receiving energy from the sun . . . The time clocks of radioactive dating were called into question. But as far as I am aware they are valid indicators of absolute time, and even before they were discovered the relative dating of the geologic sequence stood as mute testimony to evolution.

My opponent suggests that evolution must be equated with chance. Yet I see nothing in evolution that denies the laws of cause and effect operating in an orderly universe. We often use the word "chance" to indicate equal probabilities, as in the toss of a coin. Here chance is an expression of our ignorance. If we could know all, we would recognise no chance. Presumably through "special creation" anything could have been created. But it is natural selection in its interplay with the changing environment that ensures direction, in contrast to the disorder implied by the word "chance". The entire question of purpose is a distinct one that cannot be answered by reference to the course of events themselves.

I read later, in a publication of this society that is circulated to millions, my opponent's claim that he had had no difficulty in refuting my arguments.

7

Whence "creationism"?

This only have I found: God made mankind upright; but men have gone in search of many schemes.
Ecclesiastes 7:29

It was natural for pre-nineteenth century scientists to believe in special creation. Both the Bible and the current philosophic presuppositions pointed to it. But as knowledge of fossils, geological processes, extinctions, the distribution of animals and plants increased, so the traditional interpretation became more strained, and additional explanations had to be added, such as Chalmers's "gap" theory (p. 57) or Gosse's "apparent age" argument (p. 104).

Darwin's theory and marshalling of evidence in many ways released the tensions that had been building up over the understanding of the natural world, and, as we saw in chapter 2, his ideas were fairly rapidly accepted by the majority of both the scientific and Christian worlds. There were, of course, exceptions. One of the most important Christian opponents was Charles Hodge of Princeton who coined the aphorism "What is Darwinism? It is Atheism". However, Hodge was not against evolution or natural selection as such, but their effect on divinely-controlled purpose:

It is neither evolution nor natural selection which gives Darwinism its peculiar character and importance. It is that Darwin rejects all teleology, or the doctrine of final causes. He denies design in any of the organisms in the vegetable or animal world . . . and it is this feature of his system which brings it into conflict not only with Christianity, but with the fundamental principles of nature religion, it should be clearly established. [Hodge, 1874: 176–7]

It should be clear from the discussion about complementarity (p. 16f) that Hodge's condemnation came from taking too restrictive an attitude to God's activity in the world. He was, as it were, regarding mechanism and God's activity as the same thing, as his comment about natural religion indicates. Nevertheless, he was making a valid point about the perception of Darwinism. Sir George Porter, President of the Royal Society and Director of the Royal Institution, has written, "Most of our anxieties, problems and unhappiness today stem from a lack of purpose which was rare a century ago, and which can fairly be blamed on the consequences of scientific enquiry."

The popular understanding of Darwin is that he removed God and purpose from the world by making Him unnecessary as a First Cause, and if this is true, Darwin could be condemned as an agent of atheism on these grounds. But – and this is a major qualification – the correct way forward is to examine how God works in the world, rather than to assert that God is dead because evolution has happened (or conversely, that God created the world because Darwinism is untrue). We need to follow Our Lord's way and make sure that we ask the right question (p. 103).

There is no doubt that Hodge's views should be accepted as fuelling mainstream "creationism", but we need to be careful about too comprehensively claiming him as the Patron Saint of anti-evolutionism. In 1868 a Scottish Presbyterian minister, James McCosh, was appointed President of Princeton University (then known as the College of New Jersey). McCosh's reputation was based on a book *The Method of Divine Government* [1850] which taught that God governs the world both by law and through a "complication" of laws which produce "fortuities", an interpretation not too far removed from what I call "complementarity". In his first week at Princeton he told the senior students that he was fully in favour of evolution provided that it was "properly limited and explained". Later he reminisced about his time at Princeton that "I have been defending Evolution, but, in so doing, have given the proper account of it as the method of God's procedure, and find that when so understood it is in no way inconsistent with Scripture . . . We give to science the things that belong to science, and to God the things that are God's. When a scientific theory is brought before us, our first enquiry is not whether it is consistent with religion, but whether it is true."

The point of introducing McCosh here is not to indicate that Christians expounded evolutionary ideas in the early years after the publication of the *Origin*, but to record that Charles Hodge warmly welcomed McCosh to Princeton, and during the inaugural ceremony declared that never in the history of the College had an academic appointment received such universal approbation.

"Creationism" and fundamentalism

Nowadays "creationism" is taken as almost synonymous with "fundamentalism", but again we must beware about tracing modern day "creationism" to the original fundamentalists. The first fundamentalists were named on the basis of "Five Fundamentals" drawn up by the 1910 General Assembly of the American Presbyterian Church, which were intended to represent the fundamental beliefs of Protestant Christianity: the miracles of Christ; his virgin birth; his sacrifice on the cross constituting atonement for mankind's sin; his bodily resurrection; and the Bible as the directly inspired word of God. These "fundamentals" were expanded in twelve booklets published between 1910 and 1915, which included articles by James Orr (Professor of Systematic Theology in the Glasgow college of the United Free Church of Scotland) in which he argued that the Bible is not a textbook of science; that its intent is not to disclose scientific truth but to reveal the will and purpose of God; that the world is "immensely older than 6,000 years"; that the first chapter of Genesis is a "sublime poem", which science "does nothing to subvert"; and although evolution is not yet *proved*, there seems to be a growing appreciation of the strength of evidence for some form of evolutionary origin of species. George Wright, a distinguished geologist, declared forcefully that "if it should be proved that species have developed from others of a lower order as varieties are supposed to have done, it would strengthen rather than weaken the standard argument from design". Another contributor was the Princeton theologian B. B. Warfield, well-known as an authoritative defender of the authority and inerrancy of the Bible. Warfield believed that evolution could supply a tenable "theory of the method of divine providence" in the creation of mankind. He took pleasure in showing that Calvin's doctrine of the creation, "including the origination of all forms of life, vegetable and animal alike, including doubtless the bodily form of man" was a "very pure evolutionary scheme".

Clearly the fundamentalists *sensu stricto* cannot be claimed as the progenitors of "creationism". Whence, therefore, comes the movement? One of the clues must be the so-called "Tennessee Monkey Trial" of 1925 when John Scopes, a local school-teacher in Dayton, was convicted and fined $100 for violating a new law forbidding the teaching of evolution. (The sentence was later overturned on a technicality by the state appeal court because the judge had set the fine, rather than the jury as the law required.)

Scopes had not disputed the facts. While the school principal was ill, Scopes had filled in for him, using George William Hunter's *Civic Biology* – a book adopted for all schools by the State Textbook Commission. Scopes later wrote that he didn't remember if evolution had been discussed, but since biology was inseparable from evolution, he agreed he must have taught evolution. At the urging of local free thinkers and promoters, he reluctantly agreed to let his name be used to generate a court test of the constitutionality of a new state law banning evolution. He knew this would ignite a controversy.

The trial was a bigger circus than expected. The prosecutor was William Jennings Bryan, three-times Democratic presidential nominee and former Secretary of State. Before the trial he announced that it would determine whether evolution or Christianity survived. The defence lawyer was Clarence Darrow, a leading criminal lawyer, and well-known as an agnostic.

In fact, the issue was never joined legally. The judge refused to allow the defence witnesses to testify – theologians, biologists, anthropologists and palaeontologists who had come to Dayton to defend Darwinism. The issue, the judge insisted, was simply whether Scopes had taught evolution. Scopes conceded that much. Notwithstanding, Bryan wanted to make it a trial of Darwin versus the Bible, despite the judge's reluctance, and Darrow gleefully agreed. He led Bryan into illogical, untenable corners time and time again when Bryan insisted on identifying himself as an "expert" in biblical science. Bryan tried to prove that anyone could interpret Scripture, but he was no match for Darrow; and although Bryan won the case, he was humiliated and mocked in the press around the world. He refused to answer questions about the age of the earth, the antiquity of well-known archaeological sites, and so on. "I do not think about things I do not think about," said Bryan. "Do you think about things you do think about?" retorted Darrow.

Evolution was victorious if the debate were judged forensically rather than legally, and Bryan emerged a rather tarnished defender of the faith. He died a short time later, an old statesman reduced to a laughing-stock in the press, accused of leading his followers to disaster.

However, the issues did not die, because they were manifestations of concerns which Bryan personified and caricatured. They were social rather than theological. John Cole [1983] has set the scene, which places "creationism" as a symptom of fear of a changing future. The account that follows is largely in Cole's words, based on a perceptive essay by him, complemented and confirmed by Dorothy Nelkin's history of the textbook controversy [*The Creation Controversy*, 1982], and some of the articles gathered together by Ashley Montagu in a compilation called *Science and Creationism* [1984].

In the 1920s, America was changing from a nation of farmers into a nation of city dwellers and wage earners. The watershed of World War I had reduced the old empires, opening up an avenue of money and power into which much of America stepped enthusiastically. As the only industrial nation not devastated by the war, America was suddenly *the* world power – a role she had rehearsed in the Spanish-American War and in a series of Caribbean and Central American interventions. As a consequence, rural America became outvoted, outshouted and outfinanced; the farmers saw themselves relegated to pawns in battles between railroad barons, bankers, and industrialists. William Jennings Bryan was their hero. Rural populism developed, preaching a return to the simple days of yeoman farmer and the craftsman. The Populists were thus a revitalisation movement harking back to a golden past, "anti-intellectual" in effect, because they opposed "progress" that was rending their previously comfortable (or at least familiar) social and economic fabric; industrial technology was the demon, educated people invented and ran it, and evolutionists, they thought, defended it. "Too much" education was often seen as wasteful and morally questionable, except in practical fields like medicine, agriculture, or law. By the time of the Scopes trial, populism was largely restricted to religion where God gave comfort as the political and economic system had not. From political revival with religious overtones sprang religious revival with political overtones, its secular power dormant.

Darwinism, Spencerism, socialism, and anti-evolutionism

Darwin's theory was in partial eclipse at the turn of the century because of supposed conflicts with Mendelian genetics, but evolution nevertheless was embraced by a wide range of scientists, scholars, reformers, theologians, and tycoons – including people who came to be known as "Social Darwinists", followers of Darwin's contemporary, Herbert Spencer. "Social Darwinism" was Spencer's attempt to synthesise biology, physics, sociology, and philosophy. It argued that whatever existed was "natural" – the rich were rich and the poor were poor because of "natural law". Spencer's explanation of society's class structure as "natural" pleased the industrial barons; many conservatives embraced evolution because they thought it showed natural change to be glacially slow and non-revolutionary. Ironically, Spencerism fitted Marx's view as well, although Marx believed the proletarist would "naturally" come to deserved power some day.

To Populists opposing change and longing for a lost past, the naturalness or inevitability of change was an abhorrent doctrine. Social Darwinism rationalised a system they hated, and Darwinism itself was threatening because it claimed to prove that the whole of nature was in flux, outside human control. The Bible's assurance that humans had dominion over nature was challenged by it. Supposed eternal realities such as the plants and the animals were not stable through time. Most of all, Darwinism matter of factly showed humans to be animals and not the centrepiece or epitome of Creation. If Man was made in God's image, was God an animal? Populism suggested that farmers had been driven out of their idyllic fields like Adam and Eve from the Garden of Eden; what would it mean if there had been no Adam or Eve or if they had been lower animals rather than near-angels? Was there no superior past to which humanity could return? Was the Garden populated only by micro-organisms? Was the personal God to be replaced for ever by a religion totally free of supernaturalism and based upon human potential as Julian Huxley had predicted in *Science and the Future of Religion*?: "Gone is the bearded Jehovah, gone is Milton's conversational God the Father, and in their place are creative first principles, emmanent spirit, divine purposes informing the slow movement of evolutionary progress and so forth" [1931:235–6].

A blunt worry was expressed by the famous Scopes era anti-evolutionist George McCready Price: "No Adam, no fall; no fall, no atonement; no atonement, no Savior." At the same time, Presbyterian Albert Johnson claimed that evolution leads "to sensuality, carnality, Bolshevism and the Red Flag".

Henry Wood Beecher and other leaders of the nineteenth-century American religious establishment embraced Herbert Spencer's evolutionism. The natural order of things was God's will, they argued. Yale's William Graham Sumner summarised the intellectual convention of the time: "Let it be understood that we cannot go outside of this alternative: liberty, *inequality*, survival of the fittest; not liberty, *equality*, survival of the unfittest." In practical terms, he said this meant "The millionaires are a product of natural selection, acting on the whole body of men to pick out those who can meet the requirements of certain work to be done. . . . It is because they are thus selected that wealth – both their own and that entrusted to them – aggregates under their hands." This was obviously welcome news to the rich but not to the poor, who were disinherited now by God as well as by an often rapacious economic system. It generated the colourful phenomenon of industrial barons claiming to be philosopher kings, writing books and articles to celebrate the congruence of God's will, natural law, and their own prosperity. In 1900 John D. Rockefeller epitomised their pious claims to virtue: "The growth of a large business is merely survival of the fittest . . . (forcing small companies out of business) is not an evil tendency in business. It is merely the working-out of a law of nature and a law of God."

Darwin, or really Spencer's Social Darwinism, accelerated a sort of trans-Atlantic rebirth of the divine right of kings, "proving" it scientifically for the age of technology. People who opposed the scientifically intellectualised social order sometimes became explicitly antiscientific. Told that both God and Darwin decreed popular misery and that evolutionary law ordained the direction in which they were "naturally" headed many resented and opposed the new doctrines of inequality. They thus rejected Darwin and turned to "conservative" churches, those not swept up in Social Darwinism. Darwin's biology was not necessarily the issue to many critics, except to the extent that Social Darwinists (including many biologists) misused it to rationalise as "natural progress" the headlong rush into brutal industrial society. Anti-evolutionist analyses of social and political ills were naïve in their understanding of the processes of history when they believed that the solution was to return to a mythical golden age. But they accurately perceived that their troubles were caused by other people, and not by the immutable will of God or nature.

To the populist anti-Spencerians, God was on their side, and evolutionism was a sin. Times and conditions might change, but the sense of security afforded by deeply held beliefs would not lose its appeal. The populist tradition, which once embraced somewhat radical political positions, gradually abandoned much of its secular programme. After World War I, the ethos of "progress" and business prosperity dominated American politics. The Great Depression severely taxed the myth of inevitable material and social progress, and the political reaction to it included adoption of ameliorative policies echoing more radical political platforms, but the basic ordering of society survived. Wealth and power accrued to an ever smaller proportion of the population, continuing the trend begun at the turn of the century during the early populist days. World War II and the postwar boom which followed furthered the trend towards centralisation of economic and political power and social integration.

But as America industrialised, urbanised, and culturally homogenised, the old populist idea that everyone (or white Protestants, at least) should totally control his own destiny – that everyone's opinion is equal – did not slacken. On the contrary, American ideology reinforced the ideal of individualistic independence from authorities and material constraints. The Horatio Alger stories of the nineteenth century reflected populist beliefs that everyone who wanted to could succeed – that average people have the skills to cope with problems without élite education. However, an increasingly technical world emerged in the twentieth century and it was less and less possible to be a yeoman farmer. The South and Midwest USA today are as dependent upon high technology as any other part of the country, and even farming has become an industrial operation. Many people still share the Populists' views and sense of alienation, but they are more likely to be wage earners in electronic companies than independent farmers or craftsmen.

It may seem paradoxical that arch-conservative politics in the USA is today often associated with anti-evolutionism and that the inheritors of the populist tradition now often endorse the New Right political cause, given the earlier conservative establishment's fondness for Spencerism. The old Populists who opposed World War I because they saw in it the results of belief in progress and technology would be amazed to see their anti-evolutionist conclusions preached from "electronic pulpits" *via* earth satellite television relays and accompanied by the message that inter-continental missiles and unbridled capitalism are God's will. Populists past and present exemplify a range of discontent whose anti-establishmentarianism can be perceptive, irrational, and bigoted at the same time. But activist right wing religious movements such as the "Moral Majority" and the political sophistication of allegedly nonpartisan groups such as the Institute for Creation Research have proved to be effective lobbies for religious and social conservatism. Their success belies the liberals' myth that the Scopes trial settled the issues of evolution, education, and the value of intellectualism.

The textbook barometer

Scopes proved to be the only person ever tried for violating the "Monkey Law" in Tennessee, and laws in other states were not enforced in succeeding decades. The derisive publicity after the trial cast "creationism" in such a foolish light, that the Tennessee and other states' anti-evolution laws failed long before they were ruled unconstitutional in the late 1960s (see p. 146). We do not know how much teachers who taught or wanted to teach evolution were harassed, or intimidated by pressure groups using the laws as formal justification, let alone how often State endorsement of "creationism" influenced people more subtly. We do, however, have an excellent barometer of public exposure to evolution in the classroom: textbook content.

Nineteen twenty-five was a watershed year. From that point on textbooks tended to remove or dilute their treatment of evolution; some publishers began the trend in 1924, just as anti-evolution laws began to proliferate in southern states. Publishers seem to have viewed the Scopes trial as a warning of the need for self-censorship to avoid loss of sales. A number of texts that were previously outspoken about the importance of evolution as the basis of modern biology played it down in their new editions. The few new texts that openly discussed evolution, such as Alfred Kinsey's *Introduction to Biology* (1926), were not adopted widely. It was the absence of controversial material rather than scientific quality that determined book adoption by school committees, and anti-evolutionists learned to bring effective pressures on the committees. Few school students learned much about evolution, beyond the fact that biologists accepted and believed it. Evolution tends to be presented to both students and public as a belief system rather than as a scientific theory that explained scientific data.

Julian Huxley [1957] predicted that "evolutionary humanism" was to be mankind's next "religion", and countless neo-Darwinians have echoed his sentiments less dramatically. Today's "scientific creationists" sometimes seize upon such rhetoric as proof that evolution is in fact a religion rather than a science, and one diametrically opposed to belief in God as well.

Until the 1950s professional evolutionists in the USA were fairly content to teach their subject to other intellectuals; they may have been offended by book-bannings, but they were largely unconcerned about school biology being generally "non"- if not "anti-" evolutionist. Then in 1957 the Russian launching of Sputnik came as a rude awakening to America. The political, economic, and military establishment panicked at the notion that Russia was apparently ahead of America in the "science race", and the result was a large-scale reappraisal of American education that resulted in a massive federal commitment of money and attention to science education. (Ironically, in 1957 the Soviet Union was only beginning to officially accept neo-Mendelian genetics, having until then followed the Lamarckian precepts of Trofim Lysenko (see pp. 101–2)). The Cold War might have thawed slightly since its peak (Stalin was dead and the McCarthyite hysteria had subsided), but fear of the Communists proved more persuasive than a positive enthusiasm for science education in the abstract. Out of the Cold War came a series of reactions in the USA whose non-intellectual genesis was epitomised by the titles of legislation, such as: the National Defense Education Act and the National Defense Foreign Languages Act.

One of the post-Sputnik responses was the Biological Sciences Curriculum Study (BSCS), created in 1959 to develop a thoroughly reformed biology curriculum for American schools. Its textbooks on cellular biology, ecology, and molecular biology appeared in 1963–1964 as completely fresh and totally evolutionary introductions to biology for high schools. The committee drew on the best professional science available rather than on the consensus-orientated, bland non-evolutionism of previous textbooks. (For example, one of the most popular non-BSCS texts of the time treated evolution only at the end of the book and used the odd term "racial development" rather than evolution.) The BSCS books quickly became popular and by 1970 were adopted by nearly half the American high schools. Professional educators liked them but some parents trusted neither the books nor the professionals. After several emotional debates, two of the three BSCS titles adopted in Texas were dropped from the "approved list" in 1969. A similar decline of BSCS use occurred in other States when textbook vigilantes raised objections.

The clearest example of the political nature of contemporary American anti-evolutionism, however, is not the BSCS project but the MACOS episode. *Man: A Course of Study*, begun in 1963 by the National Science Foundation, was published in 1970 as an introduction to evolution and behavioural/social science for elementary school students. In 1980 Ronald Reagan used MACOS in his successful presidential campaign as an example of the federal government endorsing subversive values; he asked why NSF did not instead develop curricula supporting Christian values.

MACOS books and filmstrips comprised a rather complex, expensive package for school use. No commercial publisher would touch the project because "religious groups would not endorse the teaching of this type of material," according to a spokesman for a small foundation that agreed to undertake it. By 1974, seventeen hundred school districts in forty-seven states had adopted MACOS, but in 1975 organised opposition began to assert itself, and the sales dropped by two-thirds.

MACOS asked students to study an animal (i.e. salmon) and another culture (i.e. the Netsilik Eskimos), and to compare the lives of the animal and of the people in the other culture with their own lives, focussing on questions like: What is human about humans? How did we get this way? What are our options for the future? Animal research, ethnography, and self-study were all part of the course. The combination proved explosive. Parents reacted in force:

"I will never say I came from an ape."
"Teaching that man is an animal and nothing more
  is denying the existence of God and Revelation."
"The education experts are dictating our values."
"It eliminates the beliefs, values, and allegiances
  of children, alienating them from their parents."
[Nelkin 1977:108–9]

Right-wing organisations and religious crusaders worked together to reverse previous MACOS course adoption decisions and to prevent new ones.

The New Right charged that "Secular Humanism", evolutionism, and cultural relativism were elements of a conspiracy to subvert students, substituting relativism for beliefs in nationalism, old time religion, and the natural authority of leaders, parents and traditional values. By asking students to question authorities and to discuss rather than simply memorise values, MACOS exemplified the anti-evolutionists' fears of the social implication of evolution.

In both the Scopes trial and the MACOS debate, experts asserted in vain that students should learn what is necessary to be "citizen scientists" able to cope with a world filled with problems that science could solve. But this was the horror of the humanist position – that people rather than gods or authorities were humanity's best hope. Anti-evolutionists and other conservatives, from the John Birch Society and the Heritage Foundation to the founders of "Christian Academies", fought this idea as state interference with parental rights.

"Bible-science"

In 1941 the American Scientific Affiliation was formed, to explore the relationship between science and the Christian faith. Initially it supported a literal interpretation of the Genesis creation accounts, but it gradually moved to a less literal (albeit no less avowedly Christian) stance. Then in 1961 a major event in "creationist" history took place with the publication of *The Genesis Flood*, written by a theologian, John Whitcomb, and a hydraulic engineer, Henry Morris. It was explicitly apologetic. The authors wrote, "We believe that most of the difficulties associated with the Biblical record of the Flood are basically religious, rather than scientific. The concept of such a universal judgement on man's sin and rebellion, warning as it does of another greater judgement yet to come, is profoundly offensive to the intellectual and moral pride of modern man and so he would circumvent it if at all possible."

The Genesis Flood stimulated overt "creationism"; it apparently showed a "way round" standard geology. In 1963, ten members broke away from the American Scientific Affiliation and formed the Creation Research Society. This grew rapidly and within ten years was claiming a membership of 450 voting members (with post-graduate degrees in science) and over 1,600 non-voting members. All members had to subscribe to an official Statement of Belief which summarised the basic tenets of the movement as a whole:

1. The Bible is the written Word of God, and because it is inspired throughout, all its assertions are historically and scientifically true in all the original autographs. To the student of nature this means that the account of origins in Genesis is a factual presentation of simple historical truths.
2. All basic types of living things, including man, were made by direct creative acts of God during the Creation Week described in Genesis. Whatever biological changes have occurred since Creation Week

have accomplished only changes within the original
created kinds.

3. The great Flood described in Genesis, commonly
referred to as the Noachian Flood, was an historic
event worldwide in its extent and effect.

4. We are an organisation of Christian men of science
who accept Jesus Christ as our Lord and Saviour. The
account of the special creation of Adam and Eve as one
man and woman and their subsequent fall into sin is
the basis for our belief in the necessity of a Saviour for
all mankind. Therefore, salvation can come only
through accepting Jesus Christ as our Saviour.

In 1970 Christian Heritage College and its research division, now known as the Institute for Creation Research, were established in San Diego, California. The Institute declared that it "recognises the Bible as the source of all truth and meaning of life and God as the Creator and Sustainer of all things. Its goals are to re-establish these principles in the educational and scientific worlds." It was, it claimed, the first known time in history that an educational and research centre had been founded strictly on "creationist" principles and purposes. Projects have included a search for Noah's Ark on Mount Ararat; research into fossil anomalies; field studies on inverted geological sequences; and library research in current scientific publications dealing with origins.

In public, the Institute for Creation Research presents itself as a straightforward scientific institute. In books and lectures intended for the general public, its adherents avoid mention of God and the Bible and emphasise science. Addressing believers, they tell a different story. They insist that modern geology and the theory of evolution are affronts to the Bible. In place of them they offer "scientific creationism", of which "Flood Geology" is the central dogma.

In The Genesis Flood, Whitcomb and Morris acknowledged that "Many thousands of trained geologists, most of them sincere and honest in their conviction of the correctness of their interpretation of the geologic data, present an almost unanimous verdict against the Biblical accounts of creation and the Flood." However, they insisted that such professional opinions must be misguided, since "The instructed Christian knows that the evidences for full divine inspiration of Scripture are far weightier than the evidences for any fact of science. When confronted with the consistent testimony to a universal Flood, the believer must certainly accept it as unquestionably true" [p. 118].

Why would all but a handful of geologists reject what is "unquestionably true"? Henry Morris suggested that the answer might be found in the Tower of Babel:

> Its top was a great temple shrine, emblazoned with zodiacal signs representing the host of heaven, Satan and his "principalities and powers, rulers of the darkness of this world" (Ephesians 6:12). These evil spirits there perhaps met with Nimrod and his parents, to plan their long-range strategy against God and His redemptive purposes for the post-diluvian world. This included especially the development of a non-theistic cosmology, one which could explain the origin and meaning of the universe and man without acknowledging the true God of creation. Denial of God's power and sovereignty in creation is of course foundational in the rejection of His authority in every other sphere.
>
> The solid evidence for the above sequence of events is admittedly tenuous . . . If something like this really happened, early in post-diluvian history, then Satan himself is the originator of the concept of evolution.
>
> [Morris 1975:75]

"Creationism" in Britain

In Britain, "creationism" has been a much less influential movement than in America. Evolution was not so much argued about as taken for granted, and it was taught without dissent in biology classes. An Evolution Protest

Movement (E.P.M.) was founded in 1932 with the stated aims of publishing scientific information supporting the Bible and demonstrating that the theory of evolution was not in accordance with scientific fact. But although it numbered some eminent scientists amongst its members, most of the E.P.M. literature was written by non-scientists, and the criteria for assessing truth tended to be Scripture rather than nature.

In 1966, membership of the E.P.M. was 200; stimulated by imports from America it rose to around 850 by 1970. It changed its name to the Creation Science Movement in 1980. Following a visit from Henry Morris, a Newton Scientific Association was formed in 1972. Adopting the American practice, its policy was not to include quotations from the Bible in its lectures or literature. A British Biblical Creation Society was formed in 1977 (with a membership of 700 in 1982).

The situation in Britain is very different from that in the United States of America. The extent of the difference may be illustrated by the fact that early in 1977 the English local authority of Hertfordshire upheld the dismissal of the head of one of its schools' religious education departments because he refused to teach the country's agreed syllabus, which treated the creation story as a myth. The teacher believed in a literal interpretation of Genesis, and had declared that he wanted the children to hear this other point of view. At the very same time, the local authority in Dallas, Texas, was *insisting* that the story of Adam and Eve be taught as historical fact to children in its schools (*Sunday Telegraph*, 6th February 1977). At the 1984 conference of the Biblical Creation Society, the President explicitly distanced the Society from U.S. "creationism", which he described as anti-scriptural and inconsistent [Howgate and Lewis, 1984].

Although the British "creationist" societies have only a fairly small number of members, many of the smaller "independent" churches are fiercely anti-evolutionist, almost regarding it as a condition of membership.

Meanwhile in America, the Tennessee law under which Scopes had been prosecuted in 1925 remained on the statute book until 1968 when the Federal Supreme Court ruled that an Arkansas law (similar to the Tennessee one) was unconstitutional because it sought to establish a religious doctrine, contrary to the First and Fourteenth Amendments of the U.S. Constitution.

After their Supreme Court defeat in 1968, "creationists" changed their strategy. Led by the Institute for Creation Research many "creationists", campaigned to persuade school boards to insist on the parallel teaching of both evolution and creationism. These "creationists" pruned the public editions of their textbooks and pamphlets of any references to God, Jesus or Satan. They presented "scientific creationism" as a theoretical model on a par with evolutionary biology. Students should be exposed to both models, they argued, and be allowed to make their own choice.

When badgered by opponents who refused to accept that "scientific creationism" was not a religious doctrine, the "creationists" countered that evolution was just as much a religious doctrine. Some "creationists" pressed for state (rather than local school board) requirements for teaching "scientific creationism" in public schools, and succeeded in 1981 in convincing the Arkansas and Lousiana legislatures to pass bills of a type drafted by a staff member of the Institute for Creation Research, and distributed by Paul Ellwanger of South Carolina, who insisted his draft bill was compatible with federal and all state constitutions.

These laws sought to establish "Balanced Treatment for Creation-Science and Evolution-Science". The Arkansas law was challenged in court, and the judge ruled unequivocally that creation-science was religion and not science, and therefore that the Act could not be legally enforced [Montagu, 1984]. One of the key prosecution witnesses was Dr Stephen Jay Gould of Harvard University. I had previously sent him a copy of *Adam and the Ape*, the forerunner of this book (p. 7). He wrote after the trial: "I brought it (*Adam and the Ape*) to Arkansas ready to use it in cross-examination if anyone raised charges that evolution equals atheism and I needed to demonstrate that committed Christians could be not only evolutionists, but even Darwinians. As it turned out, the opposition was so demoralised by this time that they scarcely bothered to cross-examine . . . The trial was a complete rout for the creationists."

Conclusions about "creationism"

The reasons that a person becomes an anti-evolutionist or a "creationist" may be various. Many scientists have questions over details of the evolutionary process, but these are no doubt about evolution itself. It is frankly untrue that more and more thinking people are giving up their belief in evolution. Notwithstanding it seems clear from the history in this chapter that the mainspring of American "creationism" is a simple fear of change; a fear that a challenge to the accepted framework of belief will irreparably damage that belief, never mind opening a Pandora's Box of uncontrolled social and behavioural consequences. Certainly a similar fear also possesses many individual Christians uninfluenced by American populism. However the common factor is concern that the sealed "religious" part of life might became exposed, with the necessity of working out faith in other parts of life. This is not the "fear of the Lord" to which the Bible directs us; rather it is an insecurity which has its answer in the assurance that comes from acknowledging the awesomeness of the Creator. The fear that has "creationism" as one of its symptoms produces stunted Christians, unable or unwilling to "leave the elementary teachings about Christ and go on to maturity" [Hebrews 6:1], and which encourages a ghetto mentality in the Church, not simply avoiding being "yoked together with unbelievers" [2 Corinthians 6:14] but shirking the command to "be transformed by the renewing of your mind" [Romans 12:2]. Of course there are "creationists" who are not convinced by the scientific evidence for evolution or who are persuaded of the need for particular interpretations of the Bible, but there are also many who have never examined the evidence for evolution or who have uncritic-ally accepted the "creationist" version. This book is really addressed to those who are prepared to face up to a faith which asks questions about secular philosophies and does not merely accept secondhand opinions – be they evolu-tionist or "creationist".

Anti-evolutionism is best understood as an aspect of the anti-intellectual tradition, but it has varied through time, as has intellectualism. Neither the anti-evolutionists nor the evolutionists have a monopoly on virtue. But to people who believe science can and should have a positive value to society, the occasional virtues of anti-evolutionists must be seen as accidents in the midst of a tradition glorifying non-critical acceptance of authority. The errors of scientists have been committed within a system devoted to self-analysis, testing, and self-correction rather than acceptance of the heavy hand of tradition. Today's anti-evolutionists do not specifically oppose science, but in seeming to endorse science while rejecting basic aspects of it, they foster a schizophrenic approach to the empirical world.

Some years ago some members of the British Research Scientists' Christian Fellowship (who were not "creation-ists" in the limited sense of that term) met with members of the Biblical Creation Society to identify the real points of difference between them. The outcome of that meeting was eight questions to the Biblical Creation Society. They can serve as questions to others who accept the authority of the Bible, but are uncertain how it should be applied where evolution is concerned:

1. *Principles of Interpretation of Scripture.* Assuming that two people agree on the *doctrine* of Scripture, it is worthwhile examining how much one's interpretation is influenced by an underlying systematic theology. In particular, how open or shut is the Bible about the time scale and method of creation?

2. *Creation and Providence.* Some "creationists" disting-uish between Creation and Providence, on the

grounds that Creation was finished in six days, despite the fact that the Bible seems to use the words interchangeably. God rested from his "works" for one day and then continued them (see Hebrews 4 and John 5:17). He evidently did not cease from creation in the biblical sense of that word. The distinction makes great problems for anyone who studies biology. Biologists delight in the marvellous adaptation of animals and plants to their way of life. The teeth, body shape and enormously complex digestive system of a cow is marvellously adapted to eating grass, but so are the teeth, body shape (bones, muscles, ability to spring, claws, eyes etc.), digestive system and cryptic colouration of a tiger, adapted to being a predator. If Creation is separated from Providence, though the former may have been an act of Creation, the latter was not. It only took place after the Fall when Creation was finished and we may not marvel at these as part of "Creation". But neither are they the fruit of Providence. It rules out as not part of Creation a very large proportion of the marvellous adaptations to life that every school child is taught to appreciate. The view seems to prove too much and frankly seems to be unbiblical in that the Bible speaks often of God delighting in His creatures including predators (see for instance Job 41 and Psalm 104: 21, 24). May we or may we not admire the spider's web, the chameleon's colour change and the feeding mechanisms of carnivores, from whales to sea anemones, as works of creation? If they are not works of creation, what are they biblically? It would be useful to define the term "Biblical Creation" and do so using the word creation in a biblical way.

3. *The Effects of the Fall.* Here we have very little biblical evidence to go on. Must we not learn to leave it? Is it not impossible that predators and animal death were part of the very good creation? Presumably animals are not immortal? Incidentally, even in Isaiah 65 referring to the new heaven and the new earth,

the Bible does not speak of the animals or man as immortal, but rather "the child shall die a hundred years old" and the old man is "to fill out his days". There are acute difficulties in speaking about a world in which there is constant multiplication (according to God's command), but no death. On this basis life would only have been possible on the earth for a very short time before starvation set in. Was this really God's ideal creation?

4. *Miracles.* These are often defined in a way which is different to the Bible use of the term. We need to be able to express the nature of miracles in a way which is as close as possible to distinctions actually made in the Bible.

5. *4004 B.C.* "Creationists" differ among themselves about the date of Creation. For example, William Jennings Bryan did not hold to 4004 B.C. Is not the view that the world is older than six thousand years related to secular knowledge? The "natural reading" of the time scale given by the Bible is not necessarily what it means to say, any more than the natural reading of the scientific data is necessarily what we should believe.

6. *The Age of the Earth.* There is a large body of data whose natural reading is that the earth is very old. In the history of the church, theologians have often erred by deductive thinking from biblical material into areas where they are not familiar with the data God has given us. The Galileo debate is a classical case. It is God who has given us this data for our senses and we must treat it with respect and be honest with it.

We can say that in one's personal opinion the Bible denies that the earth is older than 4004 BC and that therefore we shall find an adequate explanation of the data in due time, but is there not a danger of teaching intellectual dishonesty if we deny that the most "natural reading" of the data is different? Also, ought we to ask people to rely on a group of *scientific* arguments which are almost totally unconvincing to people in the relevant sciences? Current science may be wrong, but so may be our interpretation of the Bible.

7. *Methodology*. There is a difference between the very largely deductive methodology of systematic theologians and the far greater reliance of science on data, even when those data do not appear to fit into our scientific systems at all. Theologians are used to arguments of the kind: "If you hold X then you ought to hold Y". Scientists are much more aware of the awkwardness of facts (including biblical verses) that fail to meet their expectations. Of course, scientists can be conceited in their opinions and plain wrong. But there is a danger of deductive arguments from clear biblical teaching leading to trouble when it takes us into areas where the conclusions apparently conflict with the real state of affairs in God's world. Must we not be willing to leave many more issues based on deduction from Scripture as open questions? We really do not know what a pre-Fall world was like. We surely cannot be dogmatic on either linguistic or biblical grounds of the meaning of "day" in Genesis 1. We surely must not impose our idea of what it means to be "very good" on the world that God had made unless we have clear biblical evidence. (According to 1 Timothy 4:3 it is part of the "good creation" that we kill animals and eat their meat.)

8. *Apologetics*. Finally, a view of a post-Fall world in which many of its striking features are not "created" by God may play into the hands of the atheists. Certainly much popular apologetics based on these views seems to do so. We read articles in the popular Christian press saying something like: "it is inconceivable that God should be responsible for all these animals dying and eating one another, etc.". But whether it is anything to do with evolution or not, these animals do die. Very large numbers of species

have become extinct. The figures and facts of animals dying and of species becoming extinct are exactly the same whichever view one takes. Therefore, our apologetics must accept this state of affairs which God has brought about.

8

Lessons and implications

God has done the extraordinary in an ordinary way and he directs the minds of his servants towards it.

John Calvin

Does it make any difference whether one "believes" in evolution or not? Christians who do not believe argue that evolution detracts from the sovereignty of God by insisting that the world and man could have come into existence by mechanisms understood by scientists, and without any need for divine intervention; and that it reduces the seriousness of the Fall by inferring that man has "risen" from animal ancestors and is getting better as he learns from his mistakes. They then leave the theological arena and question whether the palaeontological and anatomical evidence can buttress a conventional acceptance of large-scale evolution. On these grounds they claim that orthodox biology teaching brainwashes or indoctrinates students by presenting a biased picture of change and relationships, and hence is bad both from an educational and from a Christian point of view.

Belief in the authority of the Bible clearly transforms one's attitude to evolution, and in particular to man. The most common belief among non-Christians is that man is nothing more than the latest dominant species, due perhaps to be replaced in the future by another form. A humanistic development of this is the version espoused by Julian Huxley, that man has reached the end of biological evolution and has now entered a phase of psycho-social evolution.

The most influential modern prophet of this way of thought was the French Jesuit palaeontologist Teilhard de Chardin who sought to graft Christianity on to secular evolutionism. His most important work, *The Phenomenon of Man* [1959], was roundly criticised by the Nobel prize-winner, Peter Medawar [1961] on the grounds of scientific woolliness and doubletalk. However, as Gareth Jones [1969] has pointed out, it has to be accepted that Teilhard was a man who took both the modern world and his Christian faith seriously:

> behind the universe, there can be only God or absurdity, and to Teilhard only God makes sense . . . What Teilhard did present to the world was twofold – a synthesis of a form of evolutionism and a form of mystical Christianity, together with the personal testimony of a very remarkable and very devout man. But the mysticism he presented overrode both empirical science and biblical Christianity. While giving the appearance of being a prophet for the mid-twentieth century, he rejected the science of today and the biblical faith relevant for today, and clung instead to the science and philosophy of the Greek heritage.
>
> Whatever may have been Teilhard's own aims, it is difficult to avoid the conclusion that what stands out most clearly in his synthesis is his naturalism at the expense of his supernaturalism; man at the expense of God; and the world at the expense of Christ (in spite of his professions to love Christ more than anything else). Herein lies the danger of Teilhardism. Its emphasis on the incarnational and cosmic Christ to the detriment of the redeeming Christ, can only lead to worship of a generalised nature-deity with consequent neglect of the transcendent triune God revealed in the Scriptures. [pp. 64–5]

James Moore has reviewed the Protestant struggle to come to terms with Darwinism in the nineteenth century. He concluded:

> Liberal Christians "tended to forget Darwinism" because their theology was unable to receive it. Instead they were attracted to theories which could transform Darwinian evolution in accordance with their conceptions of the purpose and character of God. Those who concerned themselves with preserving historic deposits of truth . . . could say with T. H. Huxley: "Not a solitary problem presents itself to the philosophical Theist at the present day, which has not existed from the time that philo sophers began to think out the logical grounds and logical consequences of Theism." *Those, on the other hand, who turned against established theological traditions, who took scant notice of historic doctrines of creation and providence, cut themselves off from Darwin's world and from the resources by which, if Darwinism were true, it could be kept a Christian world* [my italics]. (*The Post-Darwinian Controversies*, p. 350)

Our God lives!

Interpretation

The main doctrines of the Bible – the fact of sin, substitutionary atonement, inevitability of judgement – are taught explicitly and unequivocally. However, one doctrine which is less important than the facts of redemption only because of the totality of man's sin, is that of God's sustaining and continuing activity. It is this doctrine that has become obscured by the evolution controversy. The first lesson we must learn from the last 100 years of weakened testimony is to ensure that our interpretation of Scripture is both honest and consistent – honest in the sense of facing Bible fact with as little preconception as possible, and consistent with both Scripture and relevant extra-scriptural evidence.

Christians have a tragic history of trying to defend God's word rather than proclaiming it. For example, pain-killers and anaesthesia were once regarded as sinful devices to avoid the curse of the Fall; open sewers were not covered because to do so might prevent plague, and plagues were God's judgements on man; lightning conductors were insults to God, holy bells in church towers were there to keep lightning away; and so on. The first plea is therefore for sound exegesis – and the early chapters of Genesis merely illustrate and highlight this.

Creation ordinances

When God created man, He gave him certain commands:

i. Procreate offspring – Genesis 1:28
ii. Replenish the earth – Genesis 1:28
iii. Harness and utilise natural forces – Genesis 1:28
iv. Dominion over other creatures – Genesis 1:28
v. Labour: blessing, not cursing – Genesis 2:15
vi. Weekly sabbath – Genesis 2:3
vii. Monogamous marriage – Genesis 2:18 cf. Matthew 19:5
viii. Prohibition of one particular fruit – Genesis 2:17

With the exception of the last, these commands describe our reaction to the environment in its widest sense. They are set out in rather different words in the last seven of the Ten Commandments – our duty to man as opposed to God. In other words, God's rules for regulating our attitudes and behaviour go back to creation.

Now a command given at the creation can be regarded as a limitation placed upon the created object. For example, car manufacturers state in their handbooks issued to all car users "Thou shalt keep the engine topped up with oil". This is more than an arbitrary dictate; it is a necessary rule for efficient working of the car. God's creation ordinances are exactly the same – design features, not penal rulings by a despot. For example, monogamy is often said to be a social convention supported by religion which is biologically meaningless and possibly harmful. However, Desmond Morris in *The Naked Ape* (and other anthropologists) has argued that pair-bonding between individual males and females developed in the early phase of man's evolutionary history when he came down from the trees and became a savannah-living hunter. This way of life meant that the males had to hunt co-operatively, leaving the females and young unprotected. Morris suggests that individual "faithfulness" was a necessity for female security and safe development of the young. In other words, Adam and Eve were prepared by their ancestry for their life together. God was not so much laying down difficult law, but describing the characteristics of those in whom He had placed His own image. A similar interpretation comes from Elaine Morgan's women's lib. version of evolution [*The Descent of Woman*, 1972], even though she disputes Morris's understanding of man's origin.

The same consideration applies to the command about the Sabbath. Both the French and Russians after their respective revolutions attempted to replace the one day off in seven with one day off in ten. The human constitution could not stand it. Man is adapted, commanded, or designed for a seven-day week. The verb does not matter; the fact is that we are limited in our capabilities.

A word of caution must be introduced here. The creation ordinances are stated without qualification, but restrictions are later introduced. For example, man is given dominion over all creatures in Genesis 1:28. This is specifically limited by God in Genesis 9:3,4. Again, man is commanded without qualification to multiply – in ancient Israel children were regarded as a gift from God and much law was related to preserving and enlarging the family. The restraints imposed on intercourse and procreation were minimal [e.g. Exodus 19:15; Leviticus 15:24; 1 Samuel 21:4, 5] and there is no evidence, biblical or otherwise, for contraception among the Hebrews in Old Testament times. In the New Testament the only exceptions to the original command to multiply are in 1 Corinthians 7:5, 26, dealing with the particular situation in Corinth.

However, the two testaments differ markedly in their attitude to children and posterity. The Israelites were discouraged from imitating the burial rituals of surrounding peoples, who prepared the dead for life after death. Rather, a man gained a kind of immortality through his children. The worst fate that could befall him was that his name should be "cut off" by the extinction of his line. Once Christ came, the situation changed. Life and immortality were brought to light by the appearing of our Saviour Jesus Christ [2 Timothy. 1:10]. No other form of immortality is now relevant. It could be argued that, just as the Old Testament regulations regarding clean and unclean creatures seem to reach an explicit cut-off point in Peter's visions in Acts 10:9–16, so the Old Testament attitude to procreation seems to reach an implicit one in the coming of Christ.

We must not interpret the creation ordinances out of the context in which they were given, which relates to God's revelation of His own nature. We are never authorised to act towards His creation (either inanimate or animate) in ways or from motives which are foreign to that nature. Indeed, if we regard the Ten Commandments as formal descriptions of our nature given to enable us to function more efficiently, we are more likely to obey them intelligently than if we take them as mere restrictions of a distant God. One of the New Testament Greek words for salvation, *soteria*, means wholeness or health.

The Creator of mankind is also the law-giver. In past times he expressed our reliance upon Him in a series of "laws"; in modern times of man "come of age" we can understand the causal basis of *some* of these laws in terms of our evolutionary history. In time we may probably come to appreciate the meaning – and that means the wisdom – of them all. But, and this is a big but, such an interpretation of the creation ordinances depends on man having an evolutionary history. If he was created *de novo* in 4004 B.C., there is no alternative to accepting God's laws only as expression of His sovereignty with no rational basis.

The command of God to refrain from eating "of the tree

of knowledge of good and evil" [Genesis 2:17] is of another category. This injunction seems to be entirely arbitrary, if not petty; it is obviously different from the other ordinances – and because of the consequences of disobeying it, highly significant. However, if the creation ordinances be taken as describing "properties" of humans (just as a car handbook lists laws framed in terms of the "properties" of the car), this command becomes a description of our dependence upon God, a dependence which requires obedience. We have already seen that it is difficult to distinguish qualitatively between animals and humans, but the distinguishing factor seems to be one that involves obedience. This is an unfashionable doctrine and science *cannot* provide a causal basis for it.

An analogy with drug dependence may help: drug addicts can have their addiction "transferred" to other drugs, food, their doctor, even Jesus Christ – but they remain physiologically and psychologically dependent on something or somebody. In precisely the same way, we are spiritually "designed" for dependence on God and we ignore or avoid this dependence at our peril. This is expressed in a formal way in the first three of the Ten Commandments, or in Christ's words, you shall "Love the Lord your God with all your heart and with all your soul and with all your mind and with all your strength" [Mark 12:30].

God's activity

The tragedy of the continuing "creation" debate is that it has obscured the glorious irony of the Darwinian revolution: Darwin brought God back into his world from His exclusion "out there" by eighteenth- and nineteenth-century theologians. Nineteenth-century deism was inadequate; only when God is seen to be both immanent and transcendent, which is what the Bible teaches [e.g. Eph. 4:6], will Christianity become relevant once more. Science can speak only of a mechanistic causality, while the Bible speaks of a purposive one; the intellectual climate of modern mankind makes a God active in his world necessary both scientifically and theologically.

It is worth stressing this. To many people, Christianity is not so much wrong as unnecessary. There is no virtue believing in a First Cause who is impotent in the world he created. But the evolutionary controversy has forced us to recognise that any religion worth serious consideration must be one where the God is in constant control of everyday events. Our God is so often too small – he is One who has redeemed us and who is working his purpose out, but One whom we do not like to recognise in the events of everyday living. Consequently we profess a desiccated and gutless Christianity utterly divorced from that of the New Testament church, never mind that of Luther, Cranmer, Simeon, Wesley, Booth, Moody and Temple. Let us affirm: God has worked and is working through normal, scientifically analysable events (as well as through the miraculous supernatural); He is in control of our body as well as our soul; we need fear no secular discoveries because true faith is independent although complementary to them. The Royal Society was founded by men who wanted to know how God was working in the world. May that be our attitude as well!

Conclusion

We could end there. However, the relation of God to His world is too important a topic to conclude with polemic. We must extend our thinking to a proper concern for mankind's use and misuse of this "fragile space-ship, earth". This is not the place to detail the consequences of pollution and greedy exploitation. We have already noted the teaching of Scripture that the world has been committed to mankind's control and that we are intended to control it [Genesis 1:28].

Now this dominion is best understood as a mandate from God for us to work with the natural world in the role of a manager or steward, responsible as it were to a non-executive director. Jesus Himself used the analogy of an absentee landlord for God [*e.g.* Luke 12:42–48; 19: 12–27; 20:9–18; etc.]. The Bible pictures mankind in relation to nature as a shepherd, a farm manager, or a household steward. Consequently we have a real role in caring for available resources on behalf of our "employer" – a role which allows us to make use of the resources for our own needs, but does not permit us to destroy them since they are only entrusted to us for a limited period.

As long as we refuse to play the part assigned to us by God, thus long is the entire world of nature dislocated and frustrated. Since we are God's vice-gerents on earth, mankind inevitably failed in his stewardship of God's creatures from the moment he first disobeyed God and disrupted their relationship. Conversely, when man is restored into his rightful relationship with God, he automatically resumes his responsibilities to nature again Romans 8:19–23]. This is not to say that Christians are incapable of offensive ecological acts, or that they are necessarily better ecologists than non-Christians, but to assert that the relationship between humans and their environment is dependent on ethical choices – and that these are regulated by the relationship between God and individual. The significant point in the God-man-nature hierarchy is that, as a result of God's redemptive work on the cross and the work of the Spirit in individuals, higher standards are expected – and are possible – for Christians. Factory farming and environmental pollution must be judged by the same criteria as "social pollution" such as adultery, advertising and vandalism. We are physically capable of controlling their environment; the Bible teaches that we are *intended* to control it. It is the use or abuse of this responsibility for which we must answer at the judgement seat. In other words, there is a "correct" attitude to environmental problems which is illuminated by science but depends on moral choice.

This is the crux. So often we see a problem and then want to know what to do. In our relationship to the world in the widest sense there is no simple action we can take. The important thing is our attitude to an omnipotent God at work all around us. We too often insist that the world is neutral. The creation narrative insists that it is *good*: it is God's vehicle and glory. When Christians come to appreciate this in their innermost being and practise it in their everyday decisions, then, and only then will Christianity become relevant to the non-Christians we have to deal with who are insulated from reality by the plastic envelope of technology, and social security, as well as by the numbing effects of sin.

Cupitt [1984] has commented that "religion was more badly shaken when the universe went historical in the nineteenth century than it had been when the universe went mechanical in the seventeenth century". He is right, and the fault must be fairly and squarely laid on the deist theology of the preachers. Once we return to the God of the Bible who is both immanent and transcendent, we need have no theological problems with Darwin. The paradox is that Darwin should be able to help us by forcing us away from a remote, impersonal mechanical God to a living, active Father; in practice, we spend a disproportionate time arguing about evolution in defiance of the Pauline injunction [1 Timothy 1:4; 3:9]. How the Devil must relish it!

Affirmation

In this book we have had to deal with many objections and confusions to the simple doctrine of God as Creator. Hence it seems sensible to conclude by affirming some basic premises:

1. God created the world and everything in it.
2. Genesis (indeed the whole Bible) is little concerned with *how* God carried out His mighty works.
3. The scientific description of events is *complementary* and NOT contradictory to the Bible or teleological explanation. This does not mean that either is superior or over-ruling.

4. There is no scriptural reason for disbelieving that God worked through biologically-understood mechanisms of evolution by natural selection to produce the world as we see it today.

5. BUT matter, animal life, and mankind can legitimately be regarded as special creations distant from normal on-going divine creation.

6. Humans are distinguished from the animals only in their spiritual qualities. Consequently it is reasonable to suppose (and Genesis 2:7 suggests it) that God placed His image in an already existing animal.

7. In itself the Bible/evolution controversy is sterile and probably scares many young people away from Christ, but:

   a. It teaches us to recognise how much of our understanding of Scripture is derived from its true meaning and how much is mere interpretation based on uncertain preconceptions.

   b. It enables us to recognise our "design limitations" with respect to everyday problems such as sex, sabbath-keeping, family obligations, and especially obedience to God. These are expressed in Genesis as "creation ordinances" but are much more than arbitrary regulations laid down by a distant despot.

   c. Most importantly, it forces us to recognise that God is active in "normal" everyday events. In other words, that God is relevant, active and powerful, completely distinct from the transcendent watchmaker of the special creationists or the woolly immanent urge of the liberals.

B. S. Haldane spoke truly when he said, "Science cannot give an answer to the question, 'Why should I be good?'" Science cannot, but the Bible can:

FAITH *is being sure of what we hope for and certain of what we do not see . . . By* FAITH *we understand that the universe was formed at God's command . . . Therefore . . . let us throw off everything that hinders and the sin that so easily entangles, and let us run with perseverance the race marked out for us. Let us fix our eyes on Jesus, the author and perfecter of our faith.*

[Hebrews 11:1, 3; 12:1, 2]

Appendix

What to believe about miracles*

Four years ago I was one of 14 signatories of a letter to the *Times* about miracles.[1] All of us were professors of science in British universities; six were Fellows of the Royal Society. We asserted: "It is not logically valid to use science as an argument against miracles. To believe that miracles cannot happen is as much an act of faith as to believe that they can happen. We gladly accept the virgin birth, the Gospel miracles, and the resurrection of Christ as historical events . . . Miracles are unprecedented events. Whatever the current fashions in philosophy or the revelations of opinion polls may suggest, it is important to affirm that science (based as it is upon the observation of precedents) can have nothing to say on the subject. Its "laws" are only generalisations of our experience . . ."

A leading article in *Nature*[2] accepting our statement on the nature of scientific laws, dissented from our conclusion about miracles, terming them "inexplicable and irreproducible phenomena (which) do not occur – a definition by exclusion of the concept . . . the publication of Berry *et al.* provides a licence not merely for religious belief (which on other grounds is unexceptionable) but for mischievous reports of all things paranormal, from ghosts to flying saucers".

Subsequent correspondents disagreed. For example, Clarke[3] objected that "your concern not to license

---

*Repr. from *Nature* (London), **322**, no. 6077 (July 25th 1986). © Macmillan Journals Ltd.
[1] *The Times* (London) (13th July 1984).
[2] *Nature*, **310**, 171 (1984).
[3] Clarke, P. G. H., *Nature*, **311**, 502 (1984).

'mischievous reports of all things paranormal' is no doubt motivated in the interest of scientific truth, but your strategy of defining away what you find unpalatable is the antithesis of scientific"; Mackay[4] emphasised that "for the Christian believer, baseless credulity is a sin – a disservice to the God of truth. His belief in the resurrection does not stem from softness in his standards of evidence, but rather from the coherence with which (as he sees it) that particular unprecedented event fits into and makes sense of a great mass of data. . . . There is clearly no inconsistency in believing (with astonishment) in a unique event so well attested, while remaining unconvinced by spectacular stories of 'paranormal' occurrences that lack any comparable support."

The credibility of belief in miracles has resurfaced in a report of the Church of England bishops.[5] *The Times* commented: "Did the two key miracles at the centre of the Christian faith, the Virgin Birth and the Resurrection, really happen? . . . The exercise has established one thing clearly: that belief in miracles, at least where they are central to the faith, is thoroughly intellectually respectable . . ."[6]

It would be easy to decry the criteria or standards of proof accepted by the bishops, but their integrity is presumably not in doubt. It is more profitable to enquire whether miracles are really credible, and, if so, what are the circumstances where they might be expected.

Natural law

"In an earlier age, miracles would have been one of the strongest weapons in the armoury of apologetic. A man who did such things must at the very least have the power of God with him. Jesus himself is represented as using this argument when he said, 'If it is by the finger of God that I cast out demons then the Kingdom of God has come upon

---

[4] Mackay, D. M., *Nature* **311**, 502 (1984).
[5] *The Nature of Christian Belief* (Church House, London, 1986).
[6] *The Times* (London) (6 June 1986).

you' (*Luke* 11:20). For us today, by one of those twists that make up intellectual history, miracles are rather an embarrassment. We are so impressed by the regularity of the world that any story which is full of strange happenings acquires an air of fairytale and invention."[7] The historical twist referred to by Polkinghorne was an inevitable consequence of the separation of observation (or test) from interpretation, which is the essential feature of what we call science. Before the sixteenth century "how" and "why" questions were answered in much the same way: acorns fell to the ground so that new oaks might grow; rain came so crops might flourish and people feed; and so on. The realisation that the same event could be interpreted in more than one way led to an emphasis on mechanism, and therefore on the uniformity and predictability of natural events, with a consequent restricting of divine activity to the ever-decreasing gaps in knowledge. God became unnecessary, except as a rationalisation for the unexplainable.[8]

By the seventeenth century scientists were using the "laws of nature" in the modern sense, and the physical and (increasingly) the biological worlds were regarded as self-regulating *causal nexi*. God was merely the "First Cause", and could intervene in the world only by breaking or suspending the "natural laws". Locke and Hume used the determinism of Newtonian physics to argue that natural laws were inviolable, and therefore that miracles could not happen.[9] Their conclusion seemed to be vindicated in the nineteenth century when the Darwinian revolution purged from biological systems the simple notion of purpose and created pattern. And as Cupitt says, "religion was more badly shaken when the universe went historical in the nineteenth century than it had been when it went mechanical in the seventeenth century".[10] The futility of believing in a god unable to do anything exposed the

[7] Polkinghorne, J., *The Way the World Is* (SPCK, London, 1983).
[8] Coulson, C. A., *Science and Christian Belief* (Oxford University Press, 1955).
[9] Brown, C., *Miracles and the Critical Mind* (Eerdmans, Grand Rapids, 1984).
[10] Cupitt, D., *The Sea of Faith* (BBC, London, 1984).

problem that spurred the English bishops to re-affirm that miracles could happen.[11]

Miracles and mechanisms

Defenders of miracles have tended to descend into an unconvincing mysticism or an assault on determinism. A few decades ago, it was fashionable to claim that physical indeterminancy gave God enough freedom to control events. Biological indeterminancy is a live debate now, particularly in sociobiology.[12] For example, Lewontin (unlikely to argue that miracles are common or important) strongly attacked the reality of biological laws beyond "very special rules of comportment or particular physical entities . . . If we are to find biological laws that can be the models for social laws, they will surely be at the level of laws of population, laws of evolution, laws of organisation. But it is precisely such laws that are absent in biology, although many attempts have been made to erect them."[13]

However, the case for miracles does not depend on indeterminancy, since the intellectual orthodoxy stemming from Hume's underlying thesis is not as strong as it is usually made out to be. C. S. Lewis pointed this out succinctly: "We must agree with Hume that if there is absolutely 'uniform experience' against miracles, if in other words they have never happened, why then they never have. Unfortunately we know the experience against them to be uniform only if we know that all the reports of them are false. And we know the reports to be false only if we know already that miracles have never occurred. In fact, we are arguing in a circle."[14]

Exposing the fallacy of Hume's attack on miracles also

[11] Harris, M. J., *Easter in Durham* (Paternoster, Exeter, 1985).
[12] Berry, R. J., *Free to be Different* (ed. Scott, J. R. W.) Ch.5 (Marshall, Morgan & Scott, Basingstoke, 1984).
[13] Lewontin, R. C., *Population and Biology* (ed. Keyfitz, N.) Ch.1 (Ordina, Liege, 1985).
[14] Lewis, C. S., *Miracles* (Bles, London. 1974).

eveals that it is based on an unjustified assumption, that
vents having only a single cause can be fully explained if
hat cause is known. This is logically wrong. For example,
n oil painting can be "explained" in terms either of the
listribution of pigments or the intention and design of the
rtist; both explanations refer to the same physical object
ut they complement rather than conflict. In the same way,
 miracle may be the work of (say) a divine up-holder of the
hysical world rather than a false observation or unknown
ause. Such an interpretation does not depend on any
ruption into a causal network, since the determinism of
he machine is only one of the levels of the phenomenon
sensu Polanyi).[15]

"Complementary" explanations of causation are ex-
luded only by making the reductionist assumption that
 single identifiable cause is the sole effect operating in
 particular situation. This assumption is common, but
nnecessary and restrictive. Medawar has dissected this
learly: "That there is indeed a limit upon science is made
ery likely by the existence of questions that science cannot
nswer and that no conceivable advances of science would
mpower it to answer. These are the questions that
hildren ask – the 'ultimate questions' of Karl Popper. I
ave in mind such questions as: How did everything begin?
Vhat are we all here for? What is the point of living?
)octrinaire positivism – now something of a period piece –
lismissed all such questions as nonquestions or pseudo-
uestions such as only simpletons ask and only charalatans
f one kind or another profess to be able to answer. This
eremptory dismissal leaves one empty and dissatisfied
ecause the questions make sense to those who ask them,
nd the answers to those who try to give them; but
vhatever else may be in dispute, it would be universally
greed that it is not to science that we should look for
nswers. There is then a prima facie case for the existence of
 limit to scientific understanding."[16]

Polanyi, M., *Knowing and Being* (Routledge & Kegan-Paul, London, 1969).
Medawar, P., *The Limits of Science* (Harper & Row, New York, 1984).

As far as miracles are concerned, this means that they are impossible to prove or disprove on normal scientific criteria; we accept the possibility of their occurrence by faith, and equally deny them by faith. Even if we know o deduce the mechanism behind a miracle, this does no necessarily remove the miraculous element. For example the Bible tells us that the Israelites crossed the Red Sea dry-shod because "the Lord drove the sea back by a strong east wind all night and made the sea dry land" (*Exodus* 14:21); the significance of the miracle lies in its timing and place rather than its actual occurrence.

Implications

The act of faith that denies the possibility of miracles is a straightforward reductionist judgement. Miracles by themselves are always susceptible to an explanation other than the miraculous (even if they have physical manifesta tions, such as "spontaneous" healing or the Empty Tomb) so the value of the reductionist assumption can be bes tested by its implications. These were spelt out with depressing clarity in the nihilism of Jacques Monod,[17] and comprehensively answered by W. H. Thorpe[18] who ex pounded a version of the dualism of Sherrington, Eccles and Popper which is kin to the complementarity espoused above.[19]

There are implications of embracing a reductionist deter minism which impinge on two recent controversies: "cre ationism" and the definition of human life. "Creationism" is largely an insistence that God made the world in a particular way, without using "normal" evolutionary mechanisms. Part of this claim stems from a restricted inter pretation of the Bible, but it has the effect of prescribing

[17] Monod, J., *Chance and Necessity* (Collins, London, 1971).
[18] Thorpe, W. H., *Purpose in a World of Chance* (Oxford University Press, 1978).
[19] Mackay, D. M., *Freedom of Action in a Mechanistic Universe* (Cambridge University Press, 1979); *Human Science and Human Dignity* (Hodder & Stoughton, London, 1979).

at God acted in an interventionist fashion. Notwithstand-
g, it is entirely consistent with both evolutionary biology
nd Bible texts to maintain that God worked "complemen-
rily" with genetic processes so that the world is both a
usal outcome of mutation, selection, and so on, but *also*
divine creation. The "creationist" position is at odds with
oth scientific and theistic understanding.[20, 21] Individual
uman life has a physiological and genetic continuity with
at of other humans (and indeed, other animals); the *value*
f individual life lies not in genetic uniqueness (cancers and
ydatidiform moles are also genetically unique) but in
eing (in Christian language) "made in the image of God".
his *imago* is not a physical entity, and it is a category
istake to confuse it with genetic coding or mental
unction. Notwithstanding, defenders of the inviolability
f the early embryo make this precise mistake. The *imago*
a non-biological attribute, and there is no logical (or
criptural)[22] reason for assuming that it is present from
onception. If this simple point was realised, the ethical
ebate over developments in human reproduction could
roceed more sensibly.

The conventional view of miracles is that they depend on
upernatural intervention in, or suspension of, the natural
rder. Some theologians have been over-impressed with
cientific determinism, and have attempted a demytholog-
ed (miracle-free) religion. This endeavour is now un-
shionable, but it is worse than that; Nebelick called it "a
peculative device imposed on unsuspecting persons . . .
ased on false presuppositions about both science and the
ientific world view".[23] This is no help to scientists, and
n interventionalist God will always be an embarrassment
o us.

I believe that the interpretation that miracles are a
ecessary but unpreditable consequence of a God who

Midgley, M., *Evolution as a Religion* (Methuen, London, 1985).
Berry, R. J., *Epworth Rev.* **13**, 74–85 (1986).
Rogerson, J. W., *Abortion and the Sanctity of Human Life* (ed. Channer, J. H.) Ch.4
(Paternoster, Exeter, 1985).
Nebelick, H. R., *Scot. J. Theol.* **37**, 239 (1984).

172 GOD AND EVOLUTION

holds the world in being is more plausible and more scriptural than deist interventionism. This does not mean that apparent miracles should be approached with any less objectivity than we would employ for any scientific observation; our standards of evidence should be just as rigorous. Those who deny the possibility of miracles are exercising their own brand of faith; this is based on a questionable assumption, and one which creates problems with its implications. Miracles in the New Testament are described as unusual events which are wonders due to God's power, intended as signs. Confining oneself wholly to this category (leaving aside the question of whether other sorts of miracles occur), this makes at least some miracles expectable and non-capricious, and independent of any knowledge of their mechanism.

In his exposition of the "two cultures", C. P. Snow described the scorn of the one for the other as intellectual Ludditism.[24] Miracles are examples of events which may easily be denied by an illegitimate reductionist Ludditism; scientific reality will be hindered in the process. A doctrinaire disbelief in miracles is not "more scientific" than a willingness to accept that they may occur. Some years ago Sir George Porter wrote: "Most of our anxieties, problems and unhappiness today stem from a lack of purpose which was rare a century ago and which can fairly be blamed on the consequences of scientific inquiry . . . There is one great purpose for man and for us today, and that is to try to discover man's purpose by every means in our power. That is the ultimate relevance of science."[25] He was not writing specifically about miracles, but his argument applies. Miracles are not inherently impossible or unbelievable, and acceptance of their existence does not necessarily involve credulity, but does involve recognising that science has limits.

---

[24] Snow, C. P., *The Two Cultures* (Cambridge Unviersity Press, 1975).
[25] Porter, G., *The Times* (London) (21 June 1975).

Further Reading

The words of the wise are like goads, their collected sayings like firmly embedded nails – given by one Shepherd. Be warned, my son, of anything in addition to them. Of making many books there is no end, and much study wearies the body.

Ecclesiastes 12:11,12

There are a vast number of books and articles on evolution, both about evolutionary science and about the relationship between religion (particularly Christianity) and science. This is not the place to provide a complete list of literature, but I have noted the key works, as well as providing full references for all the sources mentioned in the texts (except historical books, such as Darwin's own writings).

General

The scientific understanding of evolution is described by:
Maynard Smith [1958], Scientific American [1978], Cherfas [1982], Berry [1982] and Berry and Hallam [1986]. There are many elementary books which outline the basic genetics behind evolutionary theory [e.g. Berry, 1974b, 1977].

The main "creationist" criticisms are contained in books by Whitcomb and Morris [1961] and Morris [1974 *a*].

Secular criticisms of evolution include Macbeth [1971], Hitching [1982], Rattray Taylor [1983], and Denton [1985]; more informed accounts of the current debates about evolution are provided by Maynard Smith [1982], Grene [1983], and Ridley [1985].

It is not correct to include as current "secular criticisms" older books by scientists which cite problems with evolution at a time

173

in the past, but which have since been overtaken by subsequent scientific advances [e.g. Robson and Richards, 1936; Kerkut, 1960; Moorhead & Kaplan, 1967]; notwithstanding they are frequently cited by "creationists" as if their criticisms still stand.

Books by evolutionists who are Christians

Lack [1957], Lever [1958], Spanner, [1965, 1987], Berry [1975] and Morton [1984]. Major attacks on "creationism" are contained in Kitcher [1982], Nelkin [1982], Ruse [1982], Futuyama [1983], Godfrey [1983], Montagu [1984].

Important sources for particular chapters are:

Chapter 1: Jeeves [1969], Hookyaas [1973], Henry [1978], Mackay [1978, 1979, 1980], Peacocke [1979], Burke [1985], Russell [1985].

Chapter 2: Gillespie [1951], Moore [1979], Ospovat [1981], Mayr [1982], Bowler [1984].

Chapter 3: Conservative commentaries on Genesis (or parts of it) have been produced by Young [1964, 1966], Kidner [1967] and Blocher [1984]; less conservative commentaries include Richardson [1953], Von Rad [1961] and Westerman [1984].

Chapter 4: This chapter is based largely on articles by me [Berry, 1984, 1986a]; see also Eldredge & Tattersall [1982], Grayson [1983].

Chapter 5: Mayr & Provine [1980], Berry [1982].

Chapter 6: Whitcomb & Morris [1961], Morris [1974a], Young [1982], Kitcher [1982], Montagu [1984].

Chapter 7: A major part of this chapter is derived from Cole [1983]; see also Barker [1979], Montagu [1984], Durrant [1985], Midgley [1985].

Chapter 8: Black [1970], Berry [1972a], Faricy [1982], Moltmann [1985].

References

Acworth, R., (1970) *Creation, Evolution and the Christian Faith*. 32p. London: Evangelical.

Aiello, L., (1982) *Discovering the Origins of Man*. London: Longman.

Anderson, R. S., (1982) *On Being Human*. 234p. Grand Rapids: Eerdmans.

Andrews, E. H., (1977) *Is Evolution Scientific?* Welwyn: Evangelical.

Andrews, E. H., Gitt, W., & Ouweneel, W. J., (eds). *Concepts in Creationism*. 266p. Welwyn: Evangelical.

Appleman, P., (ed.) (2nd edn, 1979) *Darwin*. 582p. New York: Norton.

Attfield, R., (1983) *The Ethics of Environmental Concern*. 220p. Oxford: Blackwell.

Baker, Sylvia (1976) *Bone of Contention*. 33p. Welwyn: Evangelical.

Barker, E., (1979) In the beginning: the battle of creationist science against evolutionism. *Social Rev. Monogr.*, **27**: 179–200.

Berry, A. C., (1987) Genes and the nature of man. *Faith & Thought*, **113**: 9–15.

Berry, R. J., (1972a) *Ecology and Ethics*. 32p. London: Inter-Varsity.

Berry, R. J., (2nd edn, 1972b) *Teach Yourself Genetics*. 167p. London: English Universities' Press.

Berry, R. J., (1977) *Inheritance and Natural History*. 350p. London: Collins New Naturalist.

Berry, R. J., (1982) *Neo-Darwinism*. 68p. London: Edward Arnold.

Berry, R. J., (1984) Genes and morals. In Jeeves, M. A. (ed.) *Behavioural Sciences: a Christian Perspective*: 59–72. Leicester: Inter-Varsity Press.

Berry, R. J., (1985) I Believe in God . . . maker of heaven and earth. In Burke, D. (ed.) *Where Christians Disagree: Creation and Evolution*: 76–108; 131–138. Leicester: Inter-Varsity Press.

Berry, R. J., (1986a) Evolution and creation. 3. The origin of man. *Epworth Review*, **13**: 74–85.

176 REFERENCES

Berry, R. J., (1986b) What to believe about miracles. *Nature* (London), **322**: 321–322.

Berry, R. J., (1987). The theology of DNA. *Anvil*, **4**: 39–49.

Berry, R. J. and Hallam, A., (1986) *The Collins Encyclopaedia of Animal Evolution*. 160p. London: Collins.

Black, J., (1970) *The Dominion of Man*. 169p. Edinburgh: University Press.

Blocher, H., (1984) *In the Beginning*. 240p. Leicester: Inter-Varsity Press.

Bowden, M., (1977) *Ape-Man – Fact or Fallacy?* 196p. Bromley: Sovereign.

Bowler, P., (1983) *The Eclipse of Darwinism*. Baltimore: Johns Hopkins University Press.

Bowler, P., (1987) *Theories of Human Evolution: A Century of Debate, 1844–1944*, 318p. Oxford: Blackwell.

Bowler, P. J., (1984) *Evolution. The History of an Idea*. 412p. Berkeley, Los Angeles and London: University of California.

Bridgstock, M., (1986a) 'But lots of creationists are scientists . . .' In Bridgstock, M., and Smith, K. (eds), *"Creationism". An Australian Perspective*: 13–14. Melbourne: Australian Skeptics.

Bridgstock, M., (1986b) Noah's Ark and a flood of absurdities. In Bridgstock, M. and Smith, K., (eds.) *"Creationism". An Australian Perspective*: 63–67. Melbourne: Australian Skeptics.

Browne, J., (1983) *The Secular Ark. Studies in the History of Biogeography*. 273p New Haven: Yale University Press.

Brunner, E., (1939) *Man in Revolt*. Guildford: Lutterworth.

Brush, S. G., (1982) Finding the age of the Earth: by physics or by faith? *J. geol. Educ.*, **30**: 34–58.

Brush, S. G., (1983) Ghosts from the nineteenth century: creationist arguments for a young earth. In Godfrey, L. R., (ed.) *Scientists Confront Creationism*: 49–84. New York and London: Norton.

Burke, D., (ed.) (1985) *Creation and Evolution*. 288p. Leicester: Inter-Varsity Press.

Calow, P., (1983) *Evolutionary Principles*. Glasgow: Blackie.

Cameron, N. M., (1983) *Evolution and the Authority of the Bible'* 123p. Exeter: Paternoster.

Charig, A. J., Greenaway, F., Milner, A. C., Walker, C. A., and Whybrow, P. J., (1986) *Archaeopteryx* is not a forgery. *Science*, New York, **232**: 622–626.

Cherfas, J., (ed.) (1982) *Darwin Up to Date*. 72p. London: New Scientist.

Clark, R. E. D., (1948) *Darwin, Before and After*. 192p. Exeter: Paternoster.

Clark, R. W., (1984) *The Survival of Charles Darwin*. 449p. London: Weidenfeld and Nicolson.

Cole, J. R., (1963) Scopes and beyond: antievolutionism and American culture. In Godfrey, L. R., (ed.) *Scientists Confront Creationism*: 13–32. New York and London: Norton.

Cracraft, J., (1982) Reflections on the Arkansas Creation Trial. *Paleobiology*, **8**: 83–89.

Cuffey, R. J., (1972) Paleontologic evidence and organic evolution. *J. Amer. sc. Affiliation*, **24**: 161, 167–174 (reprinted in Montagu, 1984: 255–182).

Cupitt, D., (1984) *The Sea of Faith*. 286p. London: BBC.

Dalrymple, G. B., (1982) Radiometric dating, geologic time, and the age of the earth. *U.S. Geological Survey*, publ. no. 325.

Dawkins, R., (1986). *The Blind Watchmaker*. 332p. London: Longman.

Day, W., (2nd edn 1984) *Genesis on Planet Earth*. 299p. New Haven and London: Yale University Press.

Denton, M., (1985) *Evolution. A theory in crisis*. 386p. London: Burnett.

Durant, J., (ed.) (1985) *Darwinism and Divinity*. 210p. Oxford: Blackwell.

Eldredge, N., and Tattersall, I., (1982) *The Myths of Human Evolution*. 197 p. New York: Columbia University Press.

Enoch, H., (1966) *Evolution or Creation*. 172p. London: Evangelical.

Faricy, R., (1982) *Wind and Sea Obey Him*. 81p. London: SCM.

Fisher, R. A., (1950) *Creative Aspects of Natural Law*. London: Cambridge University Press.

Fisher, R. A., (1954) Retrospect of the criticisms of the theory of natural selection. In Huxley, J., Hardy, A. C., and Ford, E. B., (eds.) *Evolution as a Process*: 84–89. London: Allen and Unwin.

Flew, A., (1984) *Darwinian Evolution*, 149p. London: Paladin.

Fraser, A., (1977) Radiometric dating. *Christian Graduate*, **30**: 120–127.

Futuyama, D., (1979) *Evolutionary Biology*. Sunderland Mass: Sinauer.

Futuyama, D., (1983) *Science on Trial*. 251p. New York: Pantheon.

Gillespie, N. C., (1979) *Charles Darwin and the Problem of Creation*. 201p. Chicago and London: University of Chicago Press.

Gillespie, C. C., (1951) *Genesis and Geology*. 306p. Cambridge, Mass.: Harvard.

Gish, D. T. (1978) *Evolution: The Fossils Say No!* 186p. San Diego: Creation-Life.

Gish, D., (1979) Evolution on the rocks. *Buzz Magazine*, February 1979: 21–25.

Godfrey, L. R., (ed.) (1983) *Scientists Confront Creationism*. 324p. New York: Norton.

Grayson, D. K., (1983) *The Establishment of Human Antiquity*. 262p. New York: Academic.

Greenwood, P. H., (1979) Macroevolution – myth or reality? *Biol. J. Linn. Soc.*, **12**: 293–304.

Grene, M. (ed.) (1983) *Dimensions of Darwinism*. 336p. Cambridge: University Press.

Groves, C., (1986) Did human beings evolve? In Bridgstock, M. and Smith, K. (eds.) *"Creationism". An Australian Perspective*: 39–49. Melbourne: Australian Skeptics.

Hamilton, W. D., (1963) The evolution of altruistic behaviour. *Amer. Nat.*, **97**: 354–356.

Hayward, A., (1985) *Creation and Evolution*. 232p. London. SPCK.

Henry, C. F. H., (ed.) (1978) *Horizons of Science*. 281p. New York: Harper and Row.

Hiebert, H., (1979) *Evolution: Its Collapse in View?* Alberta: Horizon.

Hitching, F., (1982) *The Neck of the Giraffe, or Where Darwin Went Wrong*. 288 p. London: Pan.

Hobhouse, L. T., (1913) *Development and Purpose; an essay towards a philosophy of evolution*. London: Macmillan.

Hodge, C., (1874) *What Is Darwinism?* New York: Scribner, Armstrong.

Hookyaas, R., (1972) *Religion and the Rise of Modern Science*. 162p. Edinburgh: Scottish Academic Press.

Howgate, M. E., and Lewis, A. J., (1984) Creationism in confusion. *Nature* (London), **311**: 703.

Hoyle, F., and Wickramsinghe, N. C., (1981) *Evolution from Space*. 176p. London: Dent.

Hull, D. L. (1973) *Darwin and his Critics*. 473p. Chicago and London: University of Chicago.

Huxley, A., (1983) Anniversary address. *Proceedings of the Royal Society of London, B*, **217**: 117–128.

Huxley, J. S., (1931) *What Dare I Think?* New York: Harper.

Huxley, J. S., (1942) *Evolution, the Modern Synthesis*. 645p. London: Allen and Unwin.

Huxley, J. S., (1957) *Religion Without Revelation*. London: Max Parrish.

REFERENCES 179

Huxley, J., and Kettlewell, H. B. D., (1965) *Charles Darwin and His World*. 144p. London: Thames and Hudson.

Jeeves, M., (1969) *The Scientific Enterprise and Christian Faith*. 168p. London: Tyndale.

Jones, A., (1981) The genetic integrity of the kinds. *Creation Science Movement Pamphlet*, no. 227. 7p.

Jones, D. G., (1969) *Teilhard de Chardin*. 72p. London: Tyndale.

Jones, J. S., and Rouhani, S., (1986) How small was the bottleneck? *Nature* (London), **319**: 449–450.

Kerkut, K. A., (1960) *Implications of Evolution*. 174p. Oxford: Pergamon.

Keynes, R. D., (ed.) (1979) *The Beagle Record*. 409p. Cambridge: University Press.

Kidner, D., (1967) *Genesis*. 224p. London: Tyndale.

Kitcher, P., (1982) *Abusing Science*. 213p. Boston: Massachusetts Institute of Technology.

Lack, D., (1957) *Evolutionary Theory and Christian Belief*. 141p. London: Methuen.

La Follette, M. C., (ed.) (1983) *Creationism, Science, and the Law. The Arkansas Case*. 236p. Cambridge, Mass. and London: Massachusetts Institute of Technology.

Lester, L. P., and Bohlin, R. G., (1984) *The Natural Limits to Biological Change*. 207 p. Grand Rapids: Zondervan.

Lever, J., (1958) *Creation and Evolution*. 244p. Grand Rapids, Michigan: International Publications.

Livingstone, D. N., (1984) The idea of design: the vicissitudes of a key concept in the Princeton response to Darwin. *Scottish Journal of Theology*, **37**: 329–357.

Lumsden, C. J., and Wilson, E. O., (1983) *Promethean Fire. Reflections on the Origins of Mind*. 216p. Cambridge, Mass. and London: Harvard University Press.

Macbeth, N., (1971) *Darwin Retried*. 178p. New York: Dell.

McDonald, H. D., (1981) *The Christian View of Man*. 149p. London: Marshall, Morgan and Scott.

Mackay, D., (1978) *Science, Chance and Providence*. 67p. Oxford: University Press.

Mackay, D., (1979) *Human Science and Human Dignity*. 126p. London: Hodder and Stoughton.

Mackay, D., (1980) *Brains, Machines and Persons*. 111 p. London: Collins.

Maynard Smith, J., (1958, 3rd edn, 1975) *The Theory of Evolution*. 344p. Harmondsworth: Penguin.

Maynard Smith, J., (1964) Group selection and kin selection. *Nature* (London), **210**: 1145–1147.

Maynard Smith, J. (ed.), (1982) *Evolution Now*. 239p. London and Basingstoke: Macmillan.

Mayr, E., (1942) *Systematics and the Origin of Species*. New York: Columbia. (Revised as *Animal Species and Evolution* (1963) Cambridge, Mass.: Harvard; and London: Oxford University Press).

Mayr, E., (1982) *The Growth of Biological Thought*. 974p. Cambridge Mass., and London: Belknap.

Mayr, E., and Provine, W. B., (1980) *The Evolutionary Synthesis*. 487p. Cambridge, Mass.: Harvard University Press.

Medawar, P., (1961) Review of *The Phenomenon of Man*. Originally published in *Mind*. Reprinted in *Art of the Soluble* (1967), 71–81. London: Methuen.

Medawar, P., (1984) *The Limits of Science*. 108p. New York: Harper and Row.

Midgley, M., (1985) *Evolution as a Religion*. 180p. London and New York: Methuen.

Mixter, R. L., (ed.) (1959) *Evolution and Christian Faith Today*. 224p. Grand Rapids: Eerdmans.

Moltmann, J. (1985) *God in Creation. An Ecological Doctrine of Creation*. 365p. London: S.C.M.

Monod, J., (1972) *Chance and Necessity*. Collins: London.

Montagu, A. (ed.) (1984) *Science and Creationism*. 416p. New York: Oxford University Press.

Montefiore, H., (ed.) (1975) *Man and Nature*. 213p. London: Collins.

Moore, J. R., (1979) *The Post-Darwinian Controversies*. 502p. Cambridge: University Press.

Moorehead, A., (1969) *Darwin and the Beagle*. 280p. London: Hamish Hamilton.

Moorhead, P. S., and Kaplan, M. M., (eds.) (1967) *Mathematical Challenges to the Neo-Darwinian Interpretation of Evolution*. 140p. Philadelphia: Wistar.

Morgan, C. L., (1923) *Emergent Evolution*. London: Williams and Norgate.

Morgan, E., (1982) *The Aquatic Ape*. 168p. London: Souvenir.

Morris, H. M., (1967) *Evolution and the Modern Christian*. 72p. Philadelphia: Presbyterian and Reformed.

Morris, H. M., (ed.) (1974a) *Scientific Creationism*. 277p. San Diego: Creation-Life.

Morris, H. M., (1974b) *The Troubled Waters of Evolution*. San Diego: Creation-Life.

Morris, H. M., (1975) *Introducing Creationism in the Public Schools*. San Diego: Creation-Life.

Morris, H. M., (1980) *King of Creation*. San Diego: Christian Literature Press.

Morris, J. D., (1980) *Tracking Those Incredible Dinosaurs*. San Diego: Creation-Life.

Morton, J. (1984). *Redeeming Creation*. 83p. Auckland: Zealandia.

Moule, C. F. D., (1964) *Man and Nature in the New Testament*. 22p. London: Athlone Press.

Nelkin, D., (1982) *The Creation Controversy. Science or Scripture in the Schools*. 242p. New York and London: Norton.

Ospovat, D., (1981) *The Development of Darwin's Theory. Natural History, Natural Theology and Natural Selection 1838–1859*. 301p. Cambridge: University Press.

Paul, C., (1980) *The Natural History of Fossils*. 292p. London: Weidenfeld and Nicolson.

Payne, D. F., (1964) *Genesis One Reconsidered*. 29p. London: Tyndale.

Peacocke, A. R., (1979) *Creation and the World of Science*. 389p. Oxford: Clarendon.

Pearce, E. K. V., (1969) *Who Was Adam?* 151p. Exeter: Paternoster.

Pollitzer, W. Z., (1980) Evolution and special creation. *American Journal of Physical Anthropology*, **53**: 329–331.

Rattray Taylor, G., (1983) *The Great Evolution Mystery*. 277p. London: Secker and Warburg.

Rendle-Short, J., (1981) *Man: Ape or Image*. 195p. Sunnybank, Queensland: Creation Science.

Rhodes, F. H. T., (1962) *The Evolution of Life*. 330p. Harmondsworth: Penguin.

Richardson, A., (1953) *Genesis 1–11*. 134p. London: S.C.M.

Ridley, M., (1985) *The Problems of Evolution*. 159p. Oxford: University Press.

Robson, G. C., and Richards, O. W., (1936) *Variation of Animals in Nature*. London: Longmans, Green.

Ruse, M., (1982) *Darwinism Defended*. 356p. Reading, Mass.: Addison-Wesley.

Russell, C. A., (1985) *Cross-currents. Interactions between Science and Faith*. 272 p. Leicester: Inter-Varsity.

Sargant, W., (1957) *Battle for the Mind*. 248p. London: Heinemann.

Schaeffer, F. A., (1973) *Genesis in Space and Time*. 167p. London: Hodder and Stoughton.

Scientific American, (1978) *Evolution*. San Francisco: Freeman.

Simpson, G. G., (1944) *Tempo and Mode in Evolution*. (Revised as *Major Features of Evolution* (1953).) New York: Columbia U.P.

Singer, P., (1981) *The Expanding Circle. Ethics and Sociobiology*. 190p. Oxford: Clarendon.

Slusher, H. S., (2nd edn 1981) *Critique of Radiometric Dating*. San Diego: Institute for Creation Research.

Spanner, D. C., (1965) *Creation and Evolution*. 61p. London: Falcon.

Spanner, D. C., (1987) *Biblical Creation and the Theory of Evolution*. 208p. Exeter: Paternoster.

Stauffer, R. C., (ed.) (1975) *Charles Darwin's Natural Selection*. 692p. Cambridge: University Press.

Tanner, W. F., (1981) Time and the rock record. *J. Amer. sc. Affiliation*, **33**: 100–105.

Teilhard de Chardin, P., (1959) *Phenomenon of Man*. 320p. London: Collins.

Temple, F., (1884) *The Relations between Religion and Science*. London: Macmillan.

Thorpe, W. H., (1961) *Biology, Psychology and Belief*. Cambridge: University Press.

Thorpe, W. H., (1974) *Animal Nature and Human Nature*. 435p. London: Methuen.

Thorpe, W. H. (1978) *Purpose in a World of Chance*. 124p. Oxford: University Press.

Thulborn, T., (1986) On the tracks of men and money. *Nature* (London), **320**: 308.

Van Till, H., (1986) *The Fourth Day of Creation*. 286p. Grand Rapids: Eerdmans.

Von Rad, G. (1961) *Genesis*. 440 p. London: SCM.

Watson, D. C. C., (1975) *The Great Brain Robbery*. Worthing: Walter.

Watson, D. C. C., (1976) *Myths and Miracles*. 119p. Worthing: Walter.

Weiner, J. S., (1971) *Man's Natural History*. 255p. London: Weidenfeld and Nicolson.

Westerman, C., (English edn, 1984) *Genesis 1–11: A Commentary*. 636p. London: SPCK.

Whitcomb, J. C., and Morris, H. M., (1961) *The Genesis Flood*. 518p. Philadelphia: Presbyterian and Reformed.

Whitehead, A. N., (1929) *Process and Reality: an Essay in Cosmology*. Cambridge: University Press.

Wilson, E. O., (1975) *Sociobiology: the New Synthesis*. 697p. Cambridge, Mass., and London: Belknap.

Wilson, E. O. (1978) *On Human Nature*. Cambridge, Mass.: Harvard University Press.

Wiseman, P. J. (1977) *Clues to Creation in Genesis*. 232p. London: Marshall, Morgan and Scott.

Wysong, R. L., (1976) *The Creation–Evolution Controversy*. Midland, Michigan: Inquiry.

Young, D. A., (1982) *Christianity and the Age of the Earth*. 188p. Grand Rapids: Zondervan.

Young, E. J., (1964) *Studies in Genesis One*. Grand Rapids: Baker.

Young, E. J., (1966) *Genesis 3*. 165p. London: Banner of Truth.

Index